CONTRIBUTIONS TO
THE FOUNDING OF THE THEORY OF
TRANSFINITE NUMBERS

GEORG CANTOR (1845–1918)

CONTRIBUTIONS TO
THE FOUNDING OF THE THEORY OF
TRANSFINITE NUMBERS

BY

GEORG CANTOR

TRANSLATED, AND PROVIDED WITH AN INTRODUCTION
AND NOTES, BY

PHILIP E. B. JOURDAIN
M.A.(Cantab.)

NEW YORK
DOVER PUBLICATIONS, INC.

*Unabridged and unaltered reprint
of the English translation first published
in 1915*

DOVER PUBLICATIONS, INC.

Printed and bound in the United States of America

PREFACE

THIS volume contains a translation of the two very important memoirs of Georg Cantor on transfinite numbers which appeared in the *Mathematische Annalen* for 1895 and 1897* under the title: "Beiträge zur Begründung der transfiniten Mengenlehre." It seems to me that, since these memoirs are chiefly occupied with the investigation of the various transfinite cardinal and ordinal numbers and not with investigations belonging to what is usually described as "the theory of aggregates" or "the theory of sets" (*Mengenlehre, théorie des ensembles*), —the elements of the sets being real or complex numbers which are imaged as geometrical "points" in space of one or more dimensions,—the title given to them in this translation is more suitable.

These memoirs are the final and logically purified statement of many of the most important results of the long series of memoirs begun by Cantor in 1870. It is, I think, necessary, if we are to appreciate the full import of Cantor's work on transfinite numbers, to have thought through and to bear in mind Cantor's earlier researches on the theory of point-aggregates. It was in these researches that the need for the

* Vol. xlvi, 1895, pp. 481-512 ; vol. xlix, 1897, pp. 207-246.

transfinite numbers first showed itself, and it is only by the study of these researches that the majority of us can annihilate the feeling of arbitrariness and even insecurity about the introduction of these numbers. Furthermore, it is also necessary to trace backwards, especially through Weierstrass, the course of those researches which led to Cantor's work. I have, then, prefixed an Introduction tracing the growth of parts of the theory of functions during the nineteenth century, and dealing, in some detail, with the fundamental work of Weierstrass and others, and with the work of Cantor from 1870 to 1895. Some notes at the end contain a short account of the developments of the theory of transfinite numbers since 1897. In these notes and in the Introduction I have been greatly helped by the information that Professor Cantor gave me in the course of a long correspondence on the theory of aggregates which we carried on many years ago.

The philosophical revolution brought about by Cantor's work was even greater, perhaps, than the mathematical one. With few exceptions, mathematicians joyfully accepted, built upon, scrutinized, and perfected the foundations of Cantor's undying theory ; but very many philosophers combated it. This seems to have been because very few understood it. I hope that this book may help to make the subject better known to both philosophers and mathematicians.

The three men whose influence on modern pure mathematics—and indirectly modern logic and the philosophy which abuts on it—is most marked are Karl Weierstrass, Richard Dedekind, and Georg Cantor. A great part of Dedekind's work has developed along a direction parallel to the work of Cantor, and it is instructive to compare with Cantor's work Dedekind's *Stetigkeit und irrationale Zahlen* and *Was sind und was sollen die Zahlen?*, of which excellent English translations have been issued by the publishers of the present book.*

There is a French translation † of these memoirs of Cantor's, but there is no English translation of them. For kind permission to make the translation, I am indebted to Messrs B. G. Teubner of Leipzig and Berlin, the publishers of the *Mathematische Annalen*.

PHILIP E. B. JOURDAIN.

* *Essays on the Theory of Numbers* (I, *Continuity and Irrational Numbers*; II, *The Nature and Meaning of Numbers*), translated by W. W. Beman, Chicago, 1901. I shall refer to this as *Essays on Number*.

† By F. Marotte, *Sur les fondements de la théorie des ensembles transfinis*, Paris, 1899.

TABLE OF CONTENTS

	PAGE
PREFACE	v
TABLE OF CONTENTS	ix
INTRODUCTION	I
CONTRIBUTIONS TO THE FOUNDING OF THE THEORY OF TRANSFINITE NUMBERS—	
ARTICLE I. (1895)	85
ARTICLE II. (1897)	137
NOTES	202
INDEX	209

CONTRIBUTIONS TO THE FOUNDING OF THE THEORY OF TRANSFINITE NUMBERS

INTRODUCTION

I

IF it is safe to trace back to any single man the origin of those conceptions with which pure mathematical analysis has been chiefly occupied during the nineteenth century and up to the present time, we must, I think, trace it back to Jean Baptiste Joseph Fourier (1768–1830). Fourier was first and foremost a physicist, and he expressed very definitely his view that mathematics only justifies itself by the help it gives towards the solution of physical problems, and yet the light that was thrown on the general conception of a function and its "continuity," of the "convergence" of infinite series, and of an integral, first began to shine as a result of Fourier's original and bold treatment of the problems of the conduction of heat. This it was that gave the impetus to the formation and development of the theories of functions. The broadminded physicist will approve of this refining

1

development of the mathematical methods which arise from physical conceptions when he reflects that mathematics is a wonderfully powerful and economically contrived means of dealing logically and conveniently with an immense complex of data, and that we cannot be sure of the logical soundness of our methods and results until we make everything about them quite definite. The pure mathematician knows that pure mathematics has an end in itself which is more allied with philosophy. But we have not to justify pure mathematics here : we have only to point out its origin in physical conceptions. But we have also pointed out that physics can justify even the most modern developments of pure mathematics.

II

During the nineteenth century, the two great branches of the theory of functions developed and gradually separated. The rigorous foundation of the results of Fourier on trigonometrical series, which was given by Dirichlet, brought forward as subjects of investigation the general conception of a (one-valued) function of a real variable and the (in particular, trigonometrical) development of functions. On the other hand, Cauchy was gradually led to recognize the importance of what was subsequently seen to be the more special conception of function of a complex variable ; and, to a great extent independently of Cauchy, Weierstrass built up his theory of analytic functions of complex variables.

These tendencies of both Cauchy and Dirichlet combined to influence Riemann; his work on the theory of functions of a complex variable carried on and greatly developed the work of Cauchy, while the intention of his "Habilitationsschrift" of 1854 was to generalize as far as possible Dirichlet's partial solution of the problem of the development of a function of a real variable in a trigonometrical series.

Both these sides of Riemann's activity left a deep impression on Hankel. In a memoir of 1870, Hankel attempted to exhibit the theory of functions of a real variable as leading, of necessity, to the restrictions and extensions from which we start in Riemann's theory of functions of a complex variable ; and yet Hankel's researches entitle him to be called the founder of the independent theory of functions of a real variable. At about the same time, Heine initiated, under the direct influence of Riemann's "Habilitationsschrift," a new series of investigations on trigonometrical series.

Finally, soon after this, we find Georg Cantor both studying Hankel's memoir and applying to theorems on the uniqueness of trigonometrical developments those conceptions of his on irrational numbers and the "derivatives" of point-aggregates or number-aggregates which developed from the rigorous treatment of such fundamental questions given by Weierstrass at Berlin in the introduction to his lectures on analytic functions. The theory of point-aggregates soon became an independent theory

of great importance, and finally, in 1882, Cantor's
"transfinite numbers" were defined independently
of the aggregates in connexion with which they first
appeared in mathematics.

III

The investigations * of the eighteenth century on
the problem of vibrating cords led to a controversy
for the following reasons.   D'Alembert maintained
that the arbitrary functions in his general integral
of the partial differential equation to which this
problem led were restricted to have certain properties which assimilate them to the analytically
representable functions then known, and which would
prevent their course being completely arbitrary at
every point.   Euler, on the other hand, argued for
the admission of certain of these "arbitrary"
functions into analysis.   Then Daniel Bernoulli
produced a solution in the form of an infinite
trigonometrical series, and claimed, on certain
physical grounds, that this solution was as general
as d'Alembert's.   As Euler pointed out, this was so
only if any arbitrary † function $\phi(x)$ were developable in a series of the form

* *Cf.* the references given in my papers in the *Archiv der Mathematik
und Physik*, 3rd series, vol. x, 1906, pp. 255–256, and *Isis*, vol. i,
1914, pp. 670–677.   Much of this Introduction is taken from my
account of "The Development of the Theory of Transfinite Numbers"
in the above-mentioned *Archiv*, 3rd series, vol. x, pp. 254–281 ;
vol. xiv, 1909, pp. 289–311 ; vol. xvi, 1910, pp. 21–43 ; vol. xxii,
1913, pp. 1–21.

† The arbitrary functions chiefly considered in this connexion by
Euler were what he called "discontinuous" functions.   This word
does not mean what we now mean (after Cauchy) by it.   *Cf.* my paper
in *Isis*, vol. i, 1914, pp. 661–703.

$$\phi(x) = \sum_{\nu} a_{\nu} \sin \frac{\nu \pi x}{l}.$$

That this was, indeed, the case, even when $\phi(x)$ is not necessarily developable in a power-series, was first shown by Fourier, who was led to study the same mathematical problem as the above one by his researches, the first of which were communicated to the French Academy in 1807, on the conduction of heat. To Fourier is due also the determination of the coefficients in trigonometric series,

$$\phi(x) = \tfrac{1}{2}b_0 + b_1 \cos x + b_2 \cos 2x + \ldots$$
$$+ a_1 \sin x + a_2 \sin 2x + \ldots,$$

in the form

$$b_{\nu} = \frac{1}{\pi} \int_{-\pi}^{+\pi} \phi(a) \cos \nu a \, da, \quad a_{\nu} = \frac{1}{\pi} \int_{-\pi}^{+\pi} \phi(a) \sin \nu a \, da.$$

This determination was probably independent of Euler's prior determination and Lagrange's analogous determination of the coefficients of a *finite* trigonometrical series. Fourier also gave a geometrical proof of the convergence of his series, which, though not formally exact, contained the germ of Dirichlet's proof.

To Peter Gustav Lejeune-Dirichlet (1805–1859) is due the first exact treatment of Fourier's series.* He expressed the sum of the first n terms of the series by a definite integral, and proved that the

---

* "Sur la convergence des séries trigonométriques qui servent à représenter une fonction arbitraire entre des limites données," *Journ. für Math.*, vol. iv, 1829, pp. 157–169; *Ges. Werke*, vol. i, pp. 117–132.

limit, when n increases indefinitely, of this integral is the function which is to be represented by the trigonometrical series, provided that the function satisfies certain conditions. These conditions were somewhat lightened by Lipschitz in 1864.

Thus, Fourier's work led to the contemplation and exact treatment of certain functions which were totally different in behaviour from algebraic functions. These last functions were, before him, tacitly considered to be the type of all functions that can occur in analysis. Henceforth it was part of the business of analysis to investigate such non-algebraoid functions.

In the first few decades of the nineteenth century there grew up a theory of more special functions of an imaginary or complex variable. This theory was known, in part at least, to Carl Friedrich Gauss (1777–1855), but he did not publish his results, and so the theory is due to Augustin Louis Cauchy (1789–1857).* Cauchy was less far-sighted and penetrating than Gauss, the theory developed slowly, and only gradually were Cauchy's prejudices against "imaginaries" overcome. Through the years from 1814 to 1846 we can trace, first, the strong influence on Cauchy's conceptions of Fourier's ideas, then the quickly increasing unsusceptibility to the ideas of others, coupled with the extraordinarily prolific nature of this narrow-minded genius. Cauchy appeared to take pride in the production of memoirs

* *Cf.* Jourdain, "The Theory of Functions with Cauchy and Gauss," *Bibl. Math.* (3), vol. vi, 1905, pp. 190–207.

at each weekly meeting of the French Academy, and it was partly, perhaps, due to this circumstance that his works are of very unequal importance. Besides that, he did not seem to perceive even approximately the immense importance of the theory of functions of a complex variable which he did so much to create. This task remained for Puiseux, Briot and Bouquet, and others, and was advanced in the most striking manner by Georg Friedrich Bernhard Riemann (1826–1866).

Riemann may have owed to his teacher Dirichlet his bent both towards the theory of potential— which was the chief instrument in his classical development (1851) of the theory of functions of a complex variable—and that of trigonometrical series. By a memoir on the representability of a function by a trigonometrical series, which was read in 1854 but only published after his death, he not only laid the foundations for all modern investigations into the theory of these series, but inspired Hermann Hankel (1839–1873) to the method of researches from which we can date the theory of functions of a real variable as an independent science. The motive of Hankel's research was provided by reflexion on the foundations of Riemann's theory of functions of a complex variable. It was Hankel's object to show how the needs of mathematics compel us to go beyond the most general conception of a function, which was implicitly formulated by Dirichlet, to introduce the complex variable, and finally to reach that conception from which Riemann started in his inaugural dissertation. For this purpose Hankel began his "Untersuchungen über die unendlich oft oscillirenden und unstetigen Functionen ; ein Beitrag zur Feststellung des Begriffes der Function überhaupt" of 1870 by a thorough examination of the various possibilities contained in Dirichlet's conception.

Riemann, in his memoir of 1854, started from the general problem of which Dirichlet had only solved a particular case : If a function is developable in a trigonometrical series, what results about the variation of the value of the function (that is to say, what is the most general way in which it can become discontinuous and have maxima and minima) when the argument varies continuously ? The argument is a real variable, for Fourier's series, as Fourier had already noticed, may converge for real x's alone. This question was not completely answered, and, perhaps in consequence of this, the work was not published in Riemann's lifetime ; but fortunately that part of it which concerns us more particularly, and which seems to fill, and more than fill, the place of Dirichlet's contemplated revision of the principles of the infinitesimal calculus, has the finality obtained by the giving of the necessary and sufficient conditions for the integrability of a function $f(x)$, which was a necessary preliminary to Riemann's investigation. Thus, Riemann was led to give the process of integration a far wider meaning than that contemplated by Cauchy or even Dirichlet, and Riemann constructed an integrable function which becomes discontinuous an infinity of times between any two limits, as close together as wished, of the independent variable, in the following manner :—If, where x is a real variable, (x) denotes the (positive or negative) excess of x over the nearest integer, or zero if x is midway between two integers, (x) is a one-valued function of x with discontinuities at the points $x = n + \frac{1}{2}$, where n is an integer (positive, negative, or zero), and with $\frac{1}{2}$ and $-\frac{1}{2}$ for upper and lower limits respectively. Further, (νx), where ν is an integer, is discontinuous at the points $\nu x = n + \frac{1}{2}$ or $x = \frac{1}{\nu}(n + \frac{1}{2})$. Consequently, the series

$$f(x) = \sum_{\nu=1}^{\infty} \frac{(\nu x)}{\nu^2},$$

where the factor $1/\nu^2$ is added to ensure convergence for all values of x, may be supposed to be discontinuous for all values of x of the form $x = p/2n$, where p is an odd integer, relatively prime to n. It was this method that was, in a certain respect, generalized by Hankel in 1870. In Riemann's example appeared an analytical expression—and therefore a " function " in Euler's sense—which, on account of its manifold singularities, allowed of no such general properties as Riemann's " functions of a complex variable," and Hankel gave a method, whose principles were suggested by this example, of forming analytical expressions with singularities at every rational point. He was thus led to state, with some reserve, that every "function" in Dirichlet's sense is also a " function " in Euler's sense.

The greatest influence on Georg Cantor seems,

however, not to have been that exercised by Riemann, Hankel, and their successors—though the work of these men is closely connected with some parts of Cantor's work,—but by Weierstrass, a contemporary of Riemann's, who attacked many of the same problems in the theory of analytic functions of complex variables by very different and more rigorous methods.

IV

Karl Weierstrass (1815–1897) has explained, in his address delivered on the occasion of his entry into the Berlin Academy in 1857, that, from the time (the winter of 1839–1840) when, under his teacher Gudermann, he made his first acquaintance with the theory of elliptic functions, he was powerfully attracted by this branch of analysis. " Now, Abel, who was accustomed to take the highest standpoint in any part of mathematics, established a theorem which comprises all those transcendents which arise from the integration of algebraic differentials, and has the same signification for these as Euler's integral has for elliptic functions . . . ; and Jacobi succeeded in demonstrating the existence of periodic functions of *many arguments*, whose fundamental properties are established in Abel's theorem, and by means of which the true meaning and real essence of this theorem could be judged. Actually to represent, and to investigate the properties of these magnitudes of a totally new kind, of which analysis has as yet no example, I regarded as one

of the principal problems of mathematics, and, as
soon as I clearly recognized the meaning and significance of this problem, resolved to devote myself
to it. Of course it would have been foolish even
to think of the solution of such a problem without
having prepared myself by a thorough study of the
means and by busying myself with less difficult
problems."

With the *ends* stated here of Weierstrass's work
we are now concerned only incidentally : it is the
means—the "thorough study" of which he spoke—
which has had a decisive influence on our subject in
common with the theory of functions. We will,
then, pass over his early work—which was only
published in 1894—on the theory of analytic
functions, his later work on the same subject, and
his theory of the Abelian functions, and examine
his immensely important work on the foundations
of arithmetic, to which he was led by the needs of
a rigorous theory of analytic functions.

We have spoken as if the ultimate aim of Weierstrass's work was the investigation of Abelian
functions. But another and more philosophical
view was expressed in his introduction to a course
of lectures delivered in the summer of 1886 and
preserved by Gosta Mittag-Leffler * : "In order to
penetrate into mathematical science it is indispensable that we should occupy ourselves with individual

* "Sur les fondements arithmétiques de la théorie des fonctions
d'après Weierstrass," *Congrès des Mathématiques à Stockholm*,
1909, p. 10.

problems which show us its extent and constitution. But the final object which we must always keep in sight is the attainment of a sound judgment on the foundations of science."

In 1859, Weierstrass began his lectures on the theory of analytic functions at the University of Berlin. The importance of this, from our present point of view, lies in the fact that he was naturally obliged to pay special attention to the systematic treatment of the theory, and consequently, to scrutinize its foundations.

In the first place, one of the characteristics of Weierstrass's theory of functions is the abolition of the method of complex integration of Cauchy and Gauss which was used by Riemann ; and, in a letter to H. A. Schwarz of October 3, 1875, Weierstrass stated his belief that, in a systematic foundation, it is better to dispense with integration, as follows :—

". . . The more I meditate upon the principles of the theory of functions,—and I do this incessantly, —the firmer becomes my conviction that this theory must be built up on the foundation of algebraic truths, and therefore that it is not the right way to proceed conversely and make use of the *transcendental* (to express myself briefly) for the establishment of simple and fundamental algebraic theorems ; however attractive may be, for example, the considerations by which Riemann discovered so many of the most important properties of algebraic functions. That to the discoverer, *quâ* discoverer,

every route is permissible, is, of course, self-evident ;
I am only thinking of the systematic establishment
of the theory."

In the second place, and what is far more important than the question of integration, the
systematic treatment, *ab initio*, of the theory of
analytic functions led Weierstrass to profound investigations in the principles of arithmetic, and the
great result of these investigations—his theory of
irrational numbers—has a significance for all mathematics which can hardly be overrated, and our
present subject may truly be said to be almost
wholly due to this theory and its development by
Cantor.

In the theory of analytic functions we often have
to use the theorem that, if we are given an infinity
of points of the complex plane in any bounded
region of this plane, there is at least one point of
the domain such that there is an infinity of the
given points in each and every neighbourhood round
it and including it.　Mathematicians used to express
this by some such rather obscure phrase as : " There
is a point near which some of the given points are
infinitely near to one another."　If we apply, for the
proof of this, the method which seems naturally to
suggest itself, and which consists in successively
halving the region or one part of the region which
contains an infinity of points,* we arrive at what is
required,—namely, the conclusion that there is a
point such that there is another point in *any* neigh-

---

* This method was first used by Bernard Bolzano in 1817.

bourhood of it, that is to say, that there is a so-called " point of condensation,"—when, and only when, we have proved that every infinite " sum " such that the sum of *any* finite number of its terms does not exceed some given finite number defines a (rational or irrational) number. The geometrical analogue of this proposition may possibly be claimed to be evident ; but if our ideal in the theory of functions—which had, even in Weierstrass's time, been regarded for long as a justified, and even as a partly attained, ideal—is to found this theory on the conception of number alone,* this proposition leads to the considerations out of which a theory of irrational numbers such as Weierstrass's is built. The theorem on the existence of at least one point of condensation was proved by Weierstsass by the method of successive subdivisions, and was specially emphasized by him.

Weierstrass, in the introduction to his lectures on analytic functions, emphasized that, when we have admitted the notion of whole number, arithmetic needs no further postulate, but can be built up in a purely logical fashion, and also that the notion of a

---

* The separation of analysis from geometry, which appeared in the work of Lagrange, Gauss, Cauchy, and Bolzano, was a consequence of the increasing tendency of mathematicians towards logical exactitude in defining their conceptions and in making their deductions, and, consequently, in discovering the limits of validity of their conceptions and methods. However, the true connexion between the founding of analysis on a purely arithmetical basis—"arithmetization," as it has been called—and logical rigour, can only be definitely and convincingly shown after the comparatively modern thesis is proved that all the concepts (including that of number) of pure mathematics are wholly logical. And this thesis is one of the most important consequences to which the theory whose growth we are describing has forced us.

one-to-one correspondence is fundamental in count-
ing.   But it is in his purely arithmetical introduction
of irrational numbers that his great divergence from
precedent comes.   This appears from a consideration
of the history of incommensurables.

The ancient Greeks discovered the existence of incommensurable geometrical magnitudes, and therefore grew to regard arithmetic and geometry as
sciences of which the analogy had not a logical
basis.   This view was also probably due, in part at
least, to an attentive consideration of the famous
arguments of Zeno.   Analytical geometry practically identified geometry with arithmetic (or rather
with *arithmetica universalis*), and, before Weierstrass, the introduction of irrational "number"
was, explicitly or implicitly, geometrical.   The
view that number has a geometrical basis was taken
by Newton and most of his successors.   To come
to the nineteenth century, Cauchy explicitly
adopted the same view.   At the beginning of his
Cours d'analyse of 1821, he defined a "limit" as
follows : "When the successive values attributed
to a variable approach a fixed value indefinitely
so as to end by differing from it as little as is
wished, this fixed value is called the '*limit*' of all
the others" ; and remarked that "thus an irrational
number is the limit of the various fractions which
furnish more and more approximate values of it."
If we consider—as, however, Cauchy does not
appear to have done, although many others have—
the latter statement as a definition, so that an

"irrational" number is defined to be the limit of certain sums of rational numbers, we presuppose that these sums *have* a limit. In another place Cauchy remarked, after defining a series u_0, u_1, u_2, . . . to be *convergent* if the sum $s_n = u_0 + u_1 + u_2 + . . . + u_{n-1}$, for values of n always increasing, approaches indefinitely a certain limit s, that, "by the above principles, in order that the series u_0, u_1, u_2, . . . may be convergent, it is necessary and sufficient that increasing values of n make the sum s_n converge indefinitely towards a fixed limit s ; in other words, it is necessary and sufficient that, for infinitely great values of n, the sums s_n, s_{n+1}, s_{n+2}, . . . differ from the limit s, and consequently from one another, by infinitely small quantities." Hence it is necessary and sufficient that the different sums $u_n + u_{n+1} + . . . + u_{n+m}$, for different m's, end, when n increases, by obtaining numerical values constantly differing from one another by less than any assigned number.

If we know that the sums s_n have a limit s, we can at once prove the necessity of this condition ; but its sufficiency (that is to say, if, for any assigned positive rational ϵ, an integer n can always be found such that

$$| s_n - s_{n+r} | < \epsilon,$$

where r is any integer, then a limit s exists) requires a previous definition of the system of real numbers, of which the supposed limit is to be one. For it is evidently a vicious circle to define a real number as the limit of a "convergent" series, as the above definition of what we mean by a "convergent" series—a series which *has* a limit—involves (unless we limit ourselves to rational limits) a previous definition of what we mean by a "real number." *

It seems, perhaps, evident to "intuition" that, if we lay off lengths s_n, s_{n+1}, . . ., for which the above condition is fulfilled, on a straight line, that a (commensurable or incommensurable) "limiting" length s exists ; and, on these grounds, we seem to be justified in designating Cauchy's theory of real number as geometrical. But such a geometrical theory is not logically convincing, and Weierstrass showed that it is unnecessary, by defining real numbers in a manner which did not depend on a process of "going to the limit."

To repeat the point briefly, we have the following logical error in all would-be arithmetical † pre-Weierstrassian introductions of irrational numbers : we start with the conception of the system of rational numbers, we define the "sum" (a limit of a sequence of rational numbers) of an *infinite* series of rational numbers, and then raise ourselves to the conception of the system of real numbers which are got by such means. The error lies in overlooking the fact that the "sum" (b) of the infinite series of

* On the attempts of Bolzano, Hankel, and Stolz to prove arithmetically, without an arithmetical theory of real numbers, the sufficiency of the above criterion, see *Ostwald's Klassiker*, No. 153, pp. 42, 95, 107.

† It must be remembered that Cauchy's theory was not one of these. Cauchy did not attempt to define real numbers arithmetically, but simply presupposed their existence on geometrical grounds.

rational numbers can only be defined when we have already defined the real numbers, of which b is one. " I believe," said Cantor,[*] *à propos* of Weierstrass's theory, "that this logical error, which was first avoided by Weierstrass, escaped notice almost universally in earlier times, and was not noticed on the ground that it is one of the rare cases in which actual errors can lead to none of the more important mistakes in calculation."

Thus, we must bear in mind that an arithmetical theory of irrationals has to define irrational numbers not as "limits" (whose existence is not always beyond question) of certain infinite processes, but in a manner prior to any possible discussion of the question in what cases these processes define limits at all.

With Weierstrass, a number was said to be "determined" if we know of what elements it is composed and how many times each element occurs in it. Considering numbers formed with the principal unit and an infinity of its aliquot parts, Weierstrass called any aggregate whose elements and the number (finite) of times each element occurs in it [†] are known a (determined) "numerical quantity" (*Zahlengrösse*). An aggregate consisting of a finite number of elements was regarded as equal to the sum of its elements, and two aggregates of a finite number of elements were regarded as equal when the respective sums of their elements are equal.

[*] *Math. Ann.*, vol. xxi, 1883, p. 566.
[†] It is not implied that the given elements are finite in number.

A rational number r was said to be contained in a numerical quantity a when we can separate from a a partial aggregate equal to r. A numerical quantity a was said to be "finite" if we could assign a rational number R such that every rational number contained in a is smaller than R. Two numerical quantities a, b were said to be "equal," when every rational number contained in a is contained in b, and *vice versa*. When a and b are not equal, there is at least one rational number which is either contained in a without being contained in b, or *vice versa* : in the first case, a was said to be "greater than" b ; in the second, a was said to be "less than" b.

Weierstrass called the numerical quantity c defined by (*i.e.* identical with) the aggregate whose elements are those which appear in a or b, each of these elements being taken a number of times equal to the number of times in which it occurs in a increased by the number of times in which it occurs in b, the "*sum*" of a and b. The "*product*" of a and b was defined to be the numerical quantity defined by the aggregate whose elements are obtained by forming in all possible manners the product of each element of a and each element of b. In the same way was defined the product of any finite number of numerical quantities.

The "sum" of an *infinite* number of numerical quantities a, b, . . . was then defined to be the aggregate (s) whose elements occur in one (at least) of a, b, . . ., each of these elements e being taken a number of times (*n*) equal to the number of times that it occurs in *a*, increased by the number of times that it occurs in *b*, and so on. In order that *s* be *finite* and determined, it is necessary that each of the elements which occurs in it occurs a finite number of times, and it is necessary and sufficient that we can assign a number N such that the sum of any finite number of the quantities *a*, *b*, . . . is less than N.

Such is the principal point of Weierstrass's theory of real numbers. It should be noticed that, with Weierstrass, the new numbers were aggregates of the numbers previously defined ; and that this view, which appears from time to time in the better text-books, has the important advantage which was first sufficiently emphasized by Russell. This advantage is that the *existence* of limits can be proved in such a theory. That is to say, it can be proved by actual construction that there *is* a number which is the limit of a certain series fulfilling the condition of "finiteness" or "convergency." When real numbers are introduced either without proper definitions, or as "creations of our minds," or, what is far worse, as "signs,"* this existence cannot be proved.

If we consider an infinite aggregate of real numbers, or comparing these numbers for the sake of picturesqueness with the points of a straight line, an infinite "point-aggregate," we have the theorem : There is, in this domain, at least one point such that there is an infinity of points of the aggre-

---

* *Cf.* Jourdain, *Math. Gazette*, Jan. 1908, vol. iv, pp. 201–209.

gate in any, arbitrarily small, neighbourhood of it. Weierstrass's proof was, as we have mentioned, by the process, named after Bolzano and him, of successively halving any one of the intervals which contains an infinity of points. This process defines a certain numerical magnitude, the "point of condensation" (*Häufungsstelle*) in question. An analogous theorem holds for the two-dimensional region of complex numbers.

Of real numerical magnitudes x, all of which are less than some finite number, there is an "upper limit," which is defined as : A numerical magnitude G which is not surpassed in magnitude by any x and is such that either certain x's are equal to G or certain x's lie within the arbitrarily small interval $(G, \ldots, G - \delta)$, the end G being excluded. Analogously for the "lower limit" g.

It must be noticed that, if we have a *finite* aggregate of x's, one of these is the upper limit, and, if the aggregate is infinite, one of them *may* be the upper limit. In this case it need not also, but of course may, be a point of condensation. If none of them is the upper limit, this limit (whose existence is proved similarly to the existence of a point of condensation, but is, in addition, *unique*) is a point of condensation. Thus, in the above explanation of the term "upper limit," we can replace the words "either certain x's" to "being excluded" by "certain x's lie in the arbitrary small interval $(G, \ldots, G - \delta)$, the end G being *included*."

The theory of the upper and lower limit of a

(general or "Dirichlet's") real one-valued function
of a real variable was also developed and emphasized
by Weierstrass, and especially the theorem : If G is
the upper limit of those values of $y = f(x)$ * which
belong to the values of x lying inside the interval
from a to b, there is, in this interval, at least one
point $x = $ X such that the upper limit of the y's
which belong to the x's in an arbitrarily small
neighbourhood of X is G ; and analogously for the
lower limit.

If the y-value corresponding to $x = $ X is G, the
upper limit is called the "maximum" of the y's
and, if $y = f(x)$ is a *continuous* function of x, the
upper limit is a maximum ; in other words, a *continuous* function attains its upper and lower limits.
That a continuous function also takes at least once
every value between these limits was proved by
Bolzano (1817) and Cauchy (1821), but the Weier-
strassian theory of real numbers first made these
proofs rigorous.†

It is of the utmost importance to realize that,
whereas until Weierstrass's time such subjects as
the theory of points of condensation of an infinite
aggregate and the theory of irrational numbers,
on which the founding of the theory of functions

* Even if y is finite for every single x of the interval $a \leq x \leq b$, all
these y's need not be, in absolute amount, less than some finite number
(for example, $f(x) = 1/x$ for $x > 0$, $f(0) = 0$, in the interval $0 \leq x \leq 1$),
but if they are (as in the case of the sum of a uniformly convergent
series), these y's have a finite upper and lower limit in the sense defined.

† There is another conception (due to Cauchy and P. du Bois-
Reymond) allied to that of upper and lower limit. With every infinite
aggregate, there are (attained) upper and lower points of condensation,
which we may call by the Latin name "*Limites.*"

INTRODUCTION 23

depends, were hardly ever investigated, and never with such important results, Weierstrass carried research into the principles of arithmetic farther than it had been carried before. But we must also realize that there were questions, such as the nature of whole number itself, to which he made no valuable contributions. These questions, though logically the first in arithmetic, were, of course, historically the last to be dealt with. Before this could happen, arithmetic had to receive a development, by means of Cantor's discovery of transfinite numbers, into a theory of *cardinal* and *ordinal* numbers, both finite and transfinite, and logic had to be sharpened, as it was by Dedekind, Frege, Peano and Russell—to a great extent owing to the needs which this theory made evident.

V

Georg Ferdinand Ludwig Philipp Cantor was born at St Petersburg on 3rd March 1845, and lived there until 1856; from 1856 to 1863 he lived in South Germany (Wiesbaden, Frankfurt a. M., and Darmstadt); and, from autumn 1863 to Easter 1869, in Berlin. He became Privatdocent at Halle a. S. in 1869, extraordinary Professor in 1872, and ordinary Professor in 1879.* When a student at Berlin, Cantor came under the influence of Weierstrass's teaching, and one of his first papers on

---

* Those memoirs of Cantor's that will be considered here more particularly, and which constitute by far the greater part of his writings, are contained in : *Journ. für Math.*, vols. lxxvii and lxxxiv, 1874 and 1878; *Math. Ann.*, vol. iv, 1871, vol. v, 1872, vol. xv, 1879, vol. xvii, 1880, vol. xx, 1882, vol. xxi, 1883.

mathematics was partly occupied with a theory of irrational numbers, in which a sequence of numbers satisfying Cauchy's condition of convergence was used instead of Weierstrass's complex of an infinity of elements satisfying a condition which, though equivalent to the above condition, is less convenient for purposes of calculation.

This theory was exposed in the course of Cantor's researches on trigonometrical series. One of the problems of the modern theory of trigonometrical series was to establish the uniqueness of a trigonometrical development. Cantor's investigations related to the proof of this uniqueness for the most general trigonometrical series, that is to say, those trigonometrical series whose coefficients are not necessarily supposed to have the (Fourier's) integral form.

In a paper of 1870, Cantor proved the theorem that, if

$$a_1, a_2, \ldots, a_\nu, \ldots \text{ and } b_1, b_2, \ldots, b_\nu, \ldots$$

are two infinite series such that the limit of

$$a_\nu \sin \nu x + b_\nu \cos \nu x,$$

for every value of x which lies in a given interval $(a < x < b)$ of the domain of real magnitudes, is zero with increasing ν, both a_ν and b_ν converge, with increasing ν, to zero. This theorem leads to a criterion for the convergence of a trigonometrical series

$$\tfrac{1}{2}b_0 + a_1 \sin x + b_1 \cos x + \ldots + a_\nu \sin \nu x + b_\nu \cos \nu x + \ldots,$$

that Riemann proved under the supposition of the integral form for the coefficients. In a paper immediately following this one, Cantor used this theorem to prove that there is only *one* representation of $f(x)$ in the form of a trigonometrical series convergent for every value of x, except, possibly, a finite number of x's; if the sums of two trigonometrical series differ for a finite number of x's, the forms of the series coincide.

In 1871, Cantor gave a simpler proof of the uniqueness of the representation, and extended this theorem to: If we have, for every value of x, a convergent representation of the value o by a trigonometrical series, the coefficients of this representation are zero. In the same year, he also gave a simpler proof of his first theorem that, if lim $(a_\nu \sin \nu x + b_\nu \cos \nu x) = o$ for $a < x < b$, then both lim a_ν and lim b_ν are zero.

In November 1871, Cantor further extended his theorem by proving that the convergence or equality of the sums of trigonometrical series may be renounced for certain *infinite* aggregates of x's in the interval o . . . 2π without the theorem ceasing to hold. To describe the structure that such an aggregate may have in this case, Cantor began with "some explanations, or rather some simple indications, intended to put in a full light the different manners in which numerical magnitudes, in number finite or infinite, can behave," in order to make the exposition of the theorem in question as short as possible.

The system A of rational numbers (including o) serves as basis for arriving at a more extended notion of numerical magnitude. The first generalization with which we meet is when we have an infinite sequence

$$(1) \qquad a_1, a_2, \ldots, a_\nu, \ldots$$

of rational numbers, given by some law, and such that, if we take the positive rational number ϵ as small as we wish, there is an integer n_1 such that

$$(2) \qquad |a_{n+m} - a_n| < \epsilon \quad (n \overline{\overline{>}} n_1),$$

whatever the positive integer m is.* This property Cantor expressed by the words, "the series (1) has a determined limit b," and remarked particularly that these words, at that point, only served to enunciate the above property of the series, and, just as we connect (1) with a special sign b, we must also attach different signs b', b'', . . ., to different series of the same species. However, because of the fact that the "limit" may be supposed to be previously defined as : the number (if such there be) b such that $|b - a_\nu|$ becomes infinitely small as ν increases, it appears better to avoid the word and say, with Heine, in his exposition of Cantor's theory, the series (a_ν) is a "number-series," or, as Cantor afterwards expressed it, (a_ν) is a "fundamental series."

* It may be proved that this condition (2) is necessary and sufficient that the sum to infinity of the series corresponding to the sequence (1) should be a "finite numerical magnitude" in Weierstrass's sense ; and consequently Cantor's theory of irrational numbers has been described as a happy modification of Weierstrass's.

Let a second series

$$(1') \qquad a'_1, a'_2, \ldots, a'_\nu, \ldots$$

have a determined limit b', we find that (1) and (1') have always one of the three relations, which exclude one another : (*a*) $a_n - a'_n$ becomes infinitely small as n increases ; (*b*) from a certain n on, it remains always greater than ϵ, where ϵ is positive and rational ; (*c*) from a certain n on, it remains always less than $-\epsilon$. In these cases we say, respectively,

$$b = b', \quad b > b', \quad \text{or} \quad b < b'.$$

Similarly, we find that (1) has only one of the three relations with a rational number a : (*a*) $a_n - a$ becomes infinitely small as n increases ; (*b*) from a certain n on, it remains always greater than ϵ ; (*c*) from a certain n on, it remains less than $-\epsilon$. We express this by

$$b = a, \quad b > a, \quad \text{or} \quad b < a,$$

respectively. Then we can prove that $b - a_n$ becomes infinitely small as n increases, which, consequently, justifies the name given to b of "limit of the series (1)."

Denoting the totality of the numerical magnitudes b by B, we can extend the elementary operations with the rational numbers to the systems A and B united. Thus the formulæ

$$b \pm b' = b'', \quad bb' = b'', \quad b/b' = b''$$

express that the relations

$$\lim (a_n \pm a'_n - a''_n) = 0, \quad \lim (a_n a'_n - a''_n) = 0,$$
$$\lim (a_n / a'_n - a''_n) = 0$$

hold respectively. We have similar definitions when one or two of the numbers belong to A.

The system A has given rise to B; by the same process B and A united give rise to a third system C. Let the series

$$(3) \qquad\qquad b_1, b_2, \ldots, b_\nu, \ldots$$

be composed of numbers from A and B (not all from A), and such that $|\ b_{n+m} - b_n\ |$ becomes infinitely small as n increases, whatever m is (this condition is determined by the preceding definitions), then (3) is said to have "a determined limit c." The definitions of equality, inequality, and the elementary operations with the members of C, or with them and those of B and A, are analogous to the above definitions. Now, whilst B and A are such that we can equate each a to a b, but not inversely, we can equate each b to a c, and inversely. "Although thus B and C can, in a certain measure, be regarded as identical, it is essential in the theory here exposed, according to which the numerical magnitude, not having in general any objectivity at first,* only appears as element of theorems which have a certain objectivity (for example, of the theory that the numerical magnitude serves as limit for the corresponding series), to maintain the abstract distinction

* This is connected with Cantor's formalistic view of real numbers (see below).

between B and C, and also that the equivalence of
b and *b'* does not mean their identity, but only
expresses a determined relation between the series
to which they refer."

After considering further systems C, D, . . ., L
of numerical magnitudes which arise successively,
as B did from A and C from A and B, Cantor dealt
with the relations of the numerical magnitudes with
the metrical geometry of the straight line. If the
distance from a fixed point O on a straight line has
a rational ratio with the unit of measure, it is
expressed by a numerical magnitude of the system
A ; otherwise, if the point is known by a construction, we can always imagine a series such as
(1) and having with the distance in question a
relation such that the points of the straight line to
which the distances a_1, a_2, . . ., a_ν, . . . refer
approach, *ad infinitum*, as ν increases, the point to
be determined. We express this by saying : The
distance from the point to be determined to the
point O is equal to *b*, where *b* is the numerical
magnitude corresponding to the series (1). We can
then prove that the conditions of equivalence,
majority, and minority of known distances agree
with those of the numerical magnitudes which
represent these distances.

It now follows without difficulty that the numerical
magnitudes of the systems C, D, . . ., are also
capable of determining the known distances. But,
to complete the connexion we observe between the
systems of numerical magnitudes and the geometry

of the straight line, an *axiom* must still be added, which runs : To each numerical magnitude belongs also, reciprocally, a determined point of the straight line whose co-ordinate is equal to this numerical magnitude.* This theorem is called an axiom, for in its nature it cannot be demonstrated generally. It also serves to give to the numerical magnitudes a certain objectivity, of which, however, they are completely independent.

We consider, now, the relations which present themselves when we are given a finite or infinite system of numerical magnitudes, or "points," as we may call them by what precedes, with greater convenience.

If we are given a system (P) of points in a finite interval, and understand by the word "limit-point" (*Grenzpunkt*) a point of the straight line (not necessarily of P) such that in any interval within which this point is contained there is an infinity of points of P, we can prove Weierstrass's theorem that, if P is infinite, it has at least one limit-point. Every point of P which is not a limit-point of P was called by Cantor an "isolated" point.

Every point, then, of the straight line either is or is not a limit-point of P ; and we have thus defined, at the same time as P, the system of its limit-points, which may be called the "first derived system" (*erste Ableitung*) P′. If P′ is not composed of a finite number of points, we can deduce, by the same

* To each numerical magnitude belongs a determined point, but to each point are related as co-ordinates numberless *equal* numerical magnitudes.

process, a second derived system P″ from P ; and, by ν analogous operations, we arrive at the notion of a νth system $P^{(\nu)}$ derived from P. If, for example, P is composed of all the points of a line whose abscissæ are rational and comprised between o and 1 (including these limits or not), P′ is composed of all the points of the interval (o . . . 1), including these limits ; and P′, P″, . . . do not differ from P. If P is composed of the points whose abscissæ are respectively

$$1, 1/2, 1/3, \ldots, 1/\nu \ldots,$$

P′ is composed of the single point o, and derivation does not give rise to any other point. It may happen—and this case alone interests us here——that, after ν operations, $P^{(\nu)}$ is composed of a finite number of points, and consequently derivation does not give rise to any other system. In this case the primitive P is said to be of the "νth species (*Art*)," and thus P′, P″, . . . are of the $(\nu-1)$th, $(\nu-2)$th, . . . species respectively.

The extended trigonometrical theorem is now : If the equation

$$0 = \tfrac{1}{2}b_0 + a_1 \sin x + b_1 \cos x + \ldots + a_\nu \sin \nu x + b_\nu \cos \nu x + \ldots$$

is satisfied for all values of x except those which correspond to the points of a system P of the νth species, where ν is an integer as great as is pleased, in the interval (o . . . 2π), then

$$b_0 = 0, \quad c_\nu = b_\nu = 0.$$

Further information as to the continuation of these researches into derivatives of point-aggregates was given in the series of papers which Cantor began in 1879 under the title " Ueber unendliche, lineare Punktmannichfaltigkeiten." Although these papers were written subsequently to Cantor's discovery (1873) of the conceptions of "enumerability" (*Abzählbarkeit*) and "power" (*Mächtigkeit*), and these conceptions formed the basis of a classification of aggregates which, together with the classification by properties of the derivatives to be described directly, was dealt with in these papers, yet, since, by Cantor's own indications,* the discovery even of derivatives of definitely infinite order was made in 1871, we shall now extract from these papers the parts concerning derivatives.

A point-aggregate P is said to be of the "first kind" (*Gattung*) and νth "species" if P$^{(\nu)}$ consists of merely a finite aggregate of points; it is said to be of the "second kind" if the series

$$P', \ P'', \ \ldots P^{(\nu)}, \ \ldots$$

is infinite. All the points of P″, P‴, . . . are always points of P′, while a point of P′ is not necessarily a point of P.

---

* In 1880, Cantor wrote of the "dialectic generation of conceptions, which always leads farther and yet remains free from all arbitrariness, necessary and logical," of the transfinite series of indices of derivatives. "I arrived at this ten years ago [this was written in May 1880]; on the occasion of my exposition of the number-conception, I did not refer to it." And in a letter to me of 31st August 1905, Professor Cantor wrote: "Was die transfiniten Ordnungszahlen betrifft, ist es mir wahrscheinlich, dass ich schon 1871 eine Vorstellung von ihnen gehabt habe. Den Begriff der Abzählbarkeit bildete ich mir erst 1873."

Some or all of the points of a continuous * interval $(a \ldots \beta)$, the extreme points being considered as belonging to the interval, may be points of P ; if none are, P is said to be quite outside $(a \ldots \beta)$. If P is (wholly or in part) contained in $(a \ldots \beta)$, a remarkable case may present itself : every interval $(\gamma \ldots \delta)$ in it, however small, may contain points of P. Then P is said to be "everywhere dense" in the interval $(a \ldots \beta)$. For example, (1) the point-aggregate whose elements are all the points of $(a \ldots \beta)$, (2) that of all the points whose abscissæ are rational, and (3) that of all the points whose abscissæ are rational numbers of the form $\pm(2n+1)/2^m$, where m and n are integers, are everywhere dense in $(a \ldots \beta)$. It results from this that, if a point-aggregate is not everywhere dense in $(a \ldots \beta)$, there must exist an interval $(\gamma \ldots \delta)$ comprised in $(a \ldots \beta)$ and in which there is no point of P. Further, if P is everywhere dense in $(a \ldots \beta)$, not only is the same true for P', but P' consists of *all* the points of $(a \ldots \beta)$. We might take this property of P' as the definition of the expression : "P is everywhere dense in $(a \ldots \beta)$."

Such a P is necessarily of the second kind, and hence a point-aggregate of the first kind is everywhere dense in no interval. As to the question whether inversely every point-aggregate of the

* At the beginning of the first paper, Cantor stated : "As we shall show later, it is on this notion [of derived aggregate] that the simplest and completest explanation respecting the determination of a continuum rests" (see below).

second kind is everywhere dense in some intervals, Cantor postponed it.

Point-aggregates of the first kind can, as we have seen, be completely characterized by the notion of derived aggregate, but for those of the second kind this notion does not suffice, and it is necessary to give it an extension which presents itself as it were of its own accord when we go deeper into the question. It may here be remarked that Paul du Bois-Reymond was led by the study of the general theory of functions to a partly similar development of the theory of aggregates, and an appreciation of its importance in the theory of functions. In 1874, he classified functions into divisions, according to the variations of the functions required in the theory of series and integrals which serve for the representation of "arbitrary" functions. He then considered certain distributions of singularities. An infinite aggregate of points which does not form a continuous line may be either such that in any line, however small, such points occur (like the points corresponding to the rational numbers), or in any part, a finite line in which are none of those points exists. In the latter case, the points are infinitely dense on nearing certain points; "for if they are infinite in number, all their distances cannot be finite. But also not all their distances in an arbitrarily small line can vanish; for, if so, the first case would occur. So their distances can be zero only in points, or, speaking more correctly, in infinitely small lines." Here we distinguish :

(1) The points k_1 condense on nearing a finite number of points k_2; (2) the points k_2 condense at a finite number of points $k_3, \ldots$ Thus, the roots of $0 = \sin 1/x$ condense near $x = 0$, those of $0 = \sin 1/\sin 1/x$ near the preceding roots, . . . The functions with such singularities fill the space between the " common " functions and the functions with singularities from point to point. Finally, du Bois-Reymond discussed integration over such a line. In a note of 1879, he remarked that Dirichlet's criterion for the integrability of a function is not sufficient, for we can also distribute intervals in an everywhere dense fashion (*pantachisch*); that is to say, we can so distribute intervals D on the interval $(-\pi \ldots +\pi)$ that in any connected portion, however small, of $(-\pi \ldots +\pi)$ connected intervals D occur. Let, now, $\phi(x)$ be 0 in these D's and 1 in the points of $(-\pi \ldots +\pi)$ not covered by D's; then $\phi(x)$ is not integrable, although any interval inside $(-\pi \ldots +\pi)$ contains lines in which it is continuous (namely, zero). "To this distribution of intervals we are led when we seek the points of condensation of infinite order whose existence I announced to Professor Cantor years ago."

Consider a series of successive intervals on the line like those bounded by the points 1, 1/2, 1/3, . . ., 1/ν, . . . ; in the interval $(1/\nu \ldots 1/(\nu+1))$ take a point-aggregate of the first kind and νth species. Now, since each term of the series of derivatives of P is contained in the preceding ones, and consequently each $P^{(\nu)}$ arises from the preceding

$P^{(\nu-1)}$ by the falling away (at most) of points,—that is to say, no new points arise,—then, if P is of the second kind, P' will be composed of two point-aggregates, Q and R ; Q consisting of those points of P which disappear by sufficient progression in the sequence P', P'', . . ., $P^{(\nu)}$, . . ., and R of the points kept in all the terms of this sequence. In the above example, R consists of the single point zero. Cantor denoted R by $P^{(\infty)}$, and called it "the derived aggregate of P of order ∞ (infinity)." The first derivative of $P^{(\infty)}$ was denoted by $P^{(\infty+1)}$, and so on for

$$P^{(\infty+2)}, \ P^{(\infty+3)}, \ . \ . \ ., \ P^{(\infty+\nu)}, \ . \ . \ .$$

Again, $P^{(\infty)}$ may have a derivative of infinite order which Cantor denoted by $P^{(2\infty)}$; and, continuing these conceptual constructions, he arrived at derivatives which are quite logically denoted by $P^{(m\infty+n)}$, where *m* and *n* are positive integers. But he went still farther, formed the aggregate of common points of all *these* derivatives, and got a derivative which he denoted $P^{(\infty^2)}$, and so on without end. Thus he got derivatives of indices

$$\nu_0\infty^{\mu} + \nu_1\infty^{\mu-1} + \ . \ . \ . \ + \nu_\mu, \ . \ . \ . \ \infty^{\infty}, \ . \ . \ . \ \infty^{\infty^{\infty}}, \ . \ . \ .$$

"Here we see a dialectic generation of conceptions,[*] which always leads yet farther, and remains both free from every arbitrariness and necessary and logical in itself."

---

[*] To this passage Cantor added the note : "I was led to this generation ten years ago [the note was written in May 1880], but when exposing my theory of the number-conception I did not refer to it."

We see that point-aggregates of the first kind are characterized by the property that $P^{(\infty)}$ has no elements, or, in symbols,

$$P^{(\infty)} \equiv 0,$$

and also the above example shows that a point-aggregate of the second kind need not be everywhere dense in any part of an interval.

In the first of his papers of 1882, Cantor extended the conceptions "derivative" and "everywhere dense" to aggregates situated in continua of n dimensions, and also gave some reflexions on the question as to under what circumstances an (infinite) aggregate is *well defined*. These reflexions, though important for the purpose of emphasizing the legitimacy of the process used for defining $P^{(\infty)}$, $P^{(2\infty)}$, ..., are more immediately connected with the conception of "power," and will thus be dealt with later. The same applies to the proof that it is possible to remove an everywhere dense aggregate from a continuum of two or more dimensions in such a way that any two points can be connected by continuous circular arcs consisting of the remaining points, so that a continuous motion may be possible in a discontinuous space. To this Cantor added a note stating that a purely arithmetical theory of magnitudes was now not only known to be possible, but also already sketched out in its leading features.

We must now turn our attention to the development of the conceptions of "enumerability" and "power," which were gradually seen to have a very close connexion with the theory of derivatives and the theory, arising from this theory, of the transfinite numbers.

In 1873, Cantor set out from the question whether the linear continuum (of real numbers) could be put in a one-one correspondence with the aggregate of whole numbers, and found the rigorous proof that this is not the case. This proof, together with a proof that the totality of real algebraic numbers can be put in such a correspondence, and hence that there exist transcendental numbers in every interval of the number-continuum, was published in 1874.

A real number ω which is a root of a non-identical equation of the form

$$(4) \qquad a_0\omega^n + a_1\omega^{n-1} + \ldots + a_n = 0,$$

where n, a_0, a_1, . . ., a_n are integers, is called a real algebraic number; we may suppose n and a_0 positive, a_0, a_1, . . ., a_n to have no common divisor, and (4) to be irreducible. The positive whole number

$$N = n - 1 + \mid a_0 \mid + \mid a_1 \mid + \ldots + \mid a_n \mid$$

may be called the "height" of ω; and to each positive integer correspond a finite number of real algebraic numbers whose height is that integer. Thus we can arrange the totality of real algebraic numbers in a simply infinite series

$$\omega_1, \omega_2, \ldots, \omega_\nu, \ldots,$$

by arranging the numbers corresponding to the

height N in order of magnitude, and then the various heights in their order of magnitude.

Suppose, now, that the totality of the real numbers in the interval $(a \ldots \beta)$, where $a < \beta$, could be arranged in the simply infinite series

(5) $\qquad u_1, u_2, \ldots, u_\nu, \ldots$

Let a', β' be the two first numbers of (5), different from one another and from a, β, and such that $a' < \beta'$; similarly, let a'', β'', where $a'' < \beta''$, be the first different numbers in $(a' \ldots \beta')$, and so on. The numbers a', a'', $\ldots$ are members of (5) whose indices increase constantly; and similarly for the numbers β', β'', $\ldots$ of decreasing magnitude. Each of the intervals $(a \ldots \beta)$, $(a' \ldots \beta')$, $(a'' \ldots \beta'')$, $\ldots$ includes all those which follow. We can then only conceive two cases : either (a) the number of intervals is finite ;—let the last be $(a^{(\nu)} \ldots \beta^{(\nu)})$; then, since there is in this interval at most one number of (5), we can take in it a number η which does not belong to (5) ;—or (b) there are infinitely many intervals. Then, since a, a', a'', $\ldots$ increase constantly without increasing *ad infinitum*, they have a certain limit $a^{(\infty)}$, and similarly β, β', β'', $\ldots$ decrease constantly towards a certain limit $\beta^{(\infty)}$. If $a^{(\infty)} = \beta^{(\infty)}$ (which always happens when applying this method to the system (ω)), we easily see that the number $\eta = a^{(\infty)}$ cannot be in (5).* If, on the contrary, $a^{(\infty)} < \beta^{(\infty)}$, every number η in

* For if it were, we would have $\eta = u_p$, p being a determined index ; but that is not possible, for u_p is not in $(a^{(p)} \ldots \beta^{(p)})$, whilst η, by definition, is.

the interval $(\alpha^{(\infty)} \ldots \beta^{(\infty)})$ or equal to one of its ends fulfils the condition of not belonging to (5).

The property of the totality of real algebraic numbers is that the system (ω) can be put in a one-to-one or (1, 1)-correspondence with the system (ν), and hence results a new proof of Liouville's theorem that, in every interval of the real numbers, there is an infinity of transcendental (non-algebraic) numbers.

This conception of (1, 1)-correspondence between aggregates was the fundamental idea in a memoir of 1877, published in 1878, in which some important theorems of this kind of relation between various aggregates were given and suggestions made of a classification of aggregates on this basis.

If two well-defined aggregates can be put into such a (1, 1)-correspondence (that is to say, if, element to element, they can be made to correspond completely and uniquely), they are said to be of the same "power" (*Mächtigkeit* *) or to be "equivalent" (*aequivalent*). When an aggregate is finite, the notion of power corresponds to that of number (*Anzahl*), for two such aggregates have the same power when, and only when, the number of their elements is the same.

A part (*Bestandteil*; any other aggregate whose elements are also elements of the original one) of a finite aggregate has always a power less than that

---

* The word "power" was borrowed from Steiner, who used it in a quite special, but allied, sense, to express that two figures can be put, element for element, in projective correspondence.

of the aggregate itself, but this is not always the case with infinite aggregates,*—for example, the series of positive integers is easily seen to have the same power as that part of it consisting of the even integers,—and hence, from the circumstance that an infinite aggregate M is part of N (or is equivalent to a part of N), we can only conclude that the power of M is less than that of N if we know that these powers are unequal.

The series of positive integers has, as is easy to show, the smallest infinite power, but the class of aggregates with this power is extraordinarily rich and extensive, comprising, for example, Dedekind's " finite corpora," Cantor's " systems of points of the νth species," all n-ple series, and the totality of real (and also complex) algebraic numbers. Further, we can easily prove that, if M is an aggregate of this first infinite power, each infinite part of M has the same power as M, and if M', M", . . . is a finite or simply infinite series of aggregates of the first power, the aggregate resulting from the union of these aggregates has also the first power.

By the preceding memoir, continuous aggregates have not the first power, but a greater one ; and Cantor proceeded to prove that the analogue, with continua, of a multiple series—a continuum of many dimensions—has the same power as a continuum of

---

* This curious property of infinite aggregates was first noticed by Bernard Bolzano, obscurely stated (" . . . two unequal lengths [may be said to] contain the same number of points ") in a paper of 1864 in which Augustus De Morgan argued for a proper infinite, and was used as a definition of "infinite" by Dedekind (independently of Bolzano and Cantor) in 1887.

one dimension. Thus it appeared that the assumption of Riemann, Helmholtz, and others that the essential characteristic of an n-ply extended continuous manifold is that its elements depend on n real, continuous, independent variables (co-ordinates), in such a way that to each element of the manifold belongs a definite system of values x_1, x_2, . . ., x_n, and reciprocally to each admissible system x_1, x_2, . . ., x_n belongs a certain element of the manifold, tacitly supposes that the correspondence of the elements and systems of values is a continuous one.* If we let this supposition drop,† we can prove that there is a (1, 1)-correspondence between the elements of the linear continuum and those of a n-ply extended continuum.

This evidently follows from the proof of the theorem : Let x_1, x_2, . . ., x_n be real, independent variables, each of which can take any value $0 \leq x \leq 1$; then to this system of n variables can be made to correspond a variable $t(0 \leq t \leq 1)$ so that to each determined value of t corresponds one system of determined values of x_1, x_2, . . ., x_n, and *vice versa*. To prove this, we set out from the known theorem that every irrational number e between 0 and 1 can be represented in one manner by an infinite continued fraction which may be written :

$$(a_1, a_2, \ldots, a_\nu, \ldots),$$

* That is to say, an infinitely small variation in position of the element implies an infinitely small variation of the variables, and reciprocally.

† In the French translation only of this memoir of Cantor's is added here : "and this happens very often in the works of these authors (Riemann and Helmholtz)." Cantor had revised this translation.

where the a's are positive integers. There is thus
a $(1, 1)$-correspondence between the e's and the
various series of a's. Consider, now, n variables,
each of which can take independently all the irrational values (and each only once) in the interval
$(0 \ldots 1)$:

$$e_1 = (a_{1, 1}, \ a_{1, 2}, \ \ldots, \ a_{1, \nu}, \ \ldots),$$
$$e_2 = (a_{2, 1}, \ a_{2, 2}, \ \ldots, \ a_{2, \nu}, \ \ldots), \ \ldots,$$
$$e_n = (a_{n, 1}, \ a_{n, 2}, \ \ldots, \ a_{n, \nu}, \ \ldots);$$

these n irrational numbers uniquely determine a
$(n + 1)$th irrational number in $(0 \ldots 1)$,

$$d = (\beta_1, \ \beta_2, \ \ldots \beta_\nu, \ \ldots),$$

if the relation between a and β :

(6) $\beta_{(\nu-1)n+\mu} = a_{\mu, \nu}$ * $(\mu = 1, 2, \ldots, n; \ \nu = 1, 2, \ldots \infty)$

is established. Inversely, such a d determines
uniquely the series of β's and, by (6), the series of
the a's, and hence, again of the e's. We have only
to show, now, that there can exist a $(1, 1)$-corre-
spondence between the irrational numbers $0 < e < 1$
and the real (irrational and rational) numbers
$0 \leqq x \leqq 1$. For this purpose, we remark that all
the rational numbers of this interval can be written
in the form of a simply infinite series

$$\phi_1, \ \phi_2, \ \ldots, \ \psi_\nu, \ \ldots †$$

---

* If we arrange the n series of a's in a double series with n rows,
this means that we are to enumerate the a's in the order $a_{1, 1}, \ a_{2, 1},$
$\ldots a_{n, 1}, \ a_{1, 2}, \ a_{2, 2}, \ \ldots,$ and that the νth term of this series
is β_ν.

† This is done most simply as follows : Let p/q be a rational number
of this interval in its lowest terms, and put $p + q = N$. To each p/q

Then in (0 . . . 1) we take any infinite series of irrational numbers $\eta_1, \eta_2, \ldots, \eta_\nu, \ldots$ (for example, $\eta_\nu = \sqrt{2}/2^\nu$), and let h take any of the values of 0 . . . 1) except the ϕ's and η's, so that

$$x \equiv \{h, \eta_\nu, \phi_\nu\}, \quad e \equiv \{h, \eta_\nu\},^*$$

and we can also write the last formula:

$$e \equiv \{h, \eta_{2\nu-1}, \eta_{2\nu}\}.$$

Now, if we write $a \backsim b$ for "the aggregate of the a's is equivalent to that of the b's," and notice that $a \backsim a$, $a \backsim b$ and $b \backsim c$ imply $a \backsim c$, and that two aggregates of equivalent aggregates of elements, where the elements of each latter aggregate have, two by two, no common element, are equivalent, we remark that

$$h \backsim h, \quad \eta_\nu \backsim \eta_{2\nu-1}, \quad \phi_\nu \backsim \phi_{2\nu},$$

and

$$x \backsim e.$$

A generalization of the above theorem to the case of $x_1, x_2, \ldots, x_\nu, \ldots$ being a simply infinite series (and thus that the continuum may be of an infinity of dimensions while remaining of the same power as the linear continuum) results from the observation that, between the double series $\{a_{\mu, \nu}\}$, where

$$e_\mu = (a_{\mu, 1}, a_{\mu, 2}, \ldots, a_{\mu, \nu}, \ldots) \text{ for } \mu = 1, 2, \ldots \infty$$

belongs a determined positive integral value of N, and to each such N belong a finite number of fractions p/q. Imagine now the numbers p/q arranged so that those which belong to smaller values of N precede those which belong to larger ones, and those for which N has the same value are arranged the greater after the smaller.

* This notation means : the aggregate of the x's is the union of those of the h's, η_ν's, and ϕ_ν's ; and analogously for that of the e's.

and the simple series $\{\beta_\lambda\}$, a $(1, 1)$-correspondence can be established * by putting

$$\lambda = \mu + (\mu + \nu - 1)(\mu + \nu - 2)/2,$$

and the function on the right has the remarkable property of representing all the positive integers, and each of them once only, when μ and ν independently take all positive integer values.

"And now that we have proved," concluded Cantor, "for a very rich and extensive field of manifolds, the property of being capable of correspondence with the points of a continuous straight line or with a part of it (a manifold of points contained in it), the question arises . . .: Into how many and what classes (if we say that manifolds of the same or different power are grouped in the same or different *classes* respectively) do linear manifolds fall ? By a process of induction, into the further description of which we will not enter here, we are led to the theorem that the number of classes is two : the one containing all manifolds susceptible of being brought to the form : *functio ipsius* ν, where ν can receive all positive integral values ; and the other containing all manifolds reducible to the form *functio ipsius* x, where x can take all the real values in the interval $(0 . . . 1)$."

In the paper of 1879 already referred to, Cantor

* Enumerate the double series $\{\alpha_{\mu, \nu}\}$ diagonally, that is to say, in the order

$$\alpha_{1, 1}, \; \alpha_{1, 2}, \; \alpha_{2, 1}, \; \alpha_{1, 3}, \; \alpha_{2, 2}, \; \alpha_{3, 1}, \; \cdot \cdot \cdot$$

The term of this series whose index is (μ, ν) is the λth, where $\lambda = 1 + 2 + 3 + \; . . . + (\mu + \nu - 2) + \mu = (\mu + \nu - 2)(\mu + \nu - 1)/2 + \mu.$

considered the classification of aggregates * both according to the properties of their derivatives and according to their powers.   After some repetitions, a rather simpler proof of the theorem that the continuum is not of the first power was given.   But, though no essentially new results on power were published until late in 1882, we must refer to the discussion (1882) of what is meant by a "well-defined" aggregate.

The conception of power † which contains, as a particular case, the notion of whole number may, said Cantor, be considered as an attribute of every "well-defined" aggregate, whatever conceivable nature its elements may have.   "An aggregate of elements belonging to any sphere of thought is said to be 'well defined' when, in consequence of its definition and of the logical principle of the excluded middle, it must be considered as intrinsically determined whether any object belonging to this sphere belongs to the aggregate or not, and, secondly, whether two objects belonging to the aggregate are equal or not, in spite of formal differences in the manner in which they are given.   In fact, we cannot, in general, effect in a sure and precise manner these determinations with the means at our disposal ; but here it is only a question of *intrinsic* determination, from which an actual or extrinsic

---

* Linear aggregates alone were considered, since all the powers of the continua of various dimensions are to be found in them.

† "That foundation of the theory of magnitudes which we may consider to be the most general genuine moment in the case of manifolds."

determination is to be developed by perfecting the auxiliary means." Thus, we can, without any doubt, conceive it to be intrinsically determined whether a number chosen at will is algebraic or not ; and yet it was only proved in 1874 that e is transcendental, and the problem with regard to π was unsolved when Cantor wrote in 1882.[*]

In this paper was first used the word "enumerable" to describe an aggregate which could be put in a (1, 1)-correspondence with the aggregate of the positive integers and is consequently of the first (infinite) power ; and here also was the important theorem : In a n-dimensional space (A) are defined an infinity of (arbitrarily small) continua of n dimensions[†] (a) separated from one another and most meeting at their boundaries ; the aggregate of the a's is enumerable.

For refer A by means of reciprocal radii vectores to an n-ply extended figure B within a $(n+1)$-dimensional infinite space A', and let the points of B have the constant distance 1 from a fixed point of A'. To every a corresponds a n-dimensional part b of B with a definite content, and the b's are enumerable, for the number of b's greater in content than an arbitrarily small number γ is finite, for their sum is less than $2^n \pi$[‡] (the content of B).[§]

---

[*] Lindemann afterwards proved that π is transcendental. In this passage, Cantor seemed to agree with Dedekind.

[†] With every a the points of its boundary are considered as belonging to it.

[‡] In the French translation (1883) of Cantor's memoir, this number was corrected to $2\pi(n+1)/2/\Gamma((n+1)/2)$.

[§] When $n=1$, the theorem is that every aggregate of intervals on a

Finally, Cantor made the interesting remark that, if we remove from an n-dimensional continuum any enumerable and everywhere-dense aggregate, the remainder ($\mathfrak{A}$), if $n \overline{\overline{>}} 2$, does not cease to be continuously connected, in the sense that any two points N, N' of $\mathfrak{A}$ can be connected by a continuous line composed of circular arcs all of whose points belong to $\mathfrak{A}$.

VI

An application of Cantor's conception of enumerability was given by a simpler method of condensation of singularities, the construction of functions having a given singularity, such as a discontinuity, at an enumerable and everywhere-dense aggregate in a given real interval. This was suggested by Weierstrass, and published by Cantor, with Weierstrass's examples, in 1882.* The method may be thus indicated : Let $\phi(x)$ be a given function with the single singularity $x = 0$, and (ω_ν) any enumerable aggregate ; put

$$f(x) = \sum_{\nu=1}^{\infty} c^\nu \phi(x - \omega_\nu),$$

where the c_ν's are so chosen that the series and those derived from it in the particular cases treated converge unconditionally and uniformly. Then

(finite or infinite) straight line which at most meet at their ends is enumerable. The end-points are consequently enumerable, but not always the derivative of this aggregate of end-points.

* In a letter to me of 29th March 1905, Professor Cantor said : "At the conception of enumerability, of which he [Weierstrass] heard from me at Berlin in the Christmas holidays of 1873, he was at first quite amazed, but one or two days passed over, [and] it became his own and helped him to an unexpected development of his wonderful theory of functions."

$f(x)$ has at all points $x = \omega_\mu$ the same kind of singularity as $\phi(x)$ at $x = 0$, and at other points behaves, in general, regularly. The singularity at $x = \omega_\mu$ is due exclusively to the *one* term of the series in which $\nu = \mu$; the aggregate (ω_ν) may be *any* enumerable aggregate and not only, as in Hankel's method, the aggregate of the rational numbers, and the superfluous and complicating oscillations produced by the occurrence of the *sine* in Hankel's functions is avoided.

The fourth (1882) of Cantor's papers "Ueber unendliche, lineare Punktmannichfaltigkeiten" contained six theorems on enumerable point-aggregates. If an aggregate Q (in a continuum of n dimensions) is such that none of its points is a limit-point,[*] it is said to be "isolated." Then, round every point of Q a sphere can be drawn which contains no other point of Q, and hence, by the above theorem on the enumerability of the aggregate of these spheres, is enumerable.

Secondly, if P′ is enumerable, P is. For let

$$\mathfrak{D}(P, P') \equiv R, \ P - R \equiv Q;[\dagger]$$

then Q is isolated and therefore enumerable, and R is also enumerable, since R is contained in P′; so P is enumerable.

The next three theorems state that, if $P^{(\nu)}$, or

---

[*] Cantor expressed this $\mathfrak{D}(Q, Q') \equiv 0$. *Cf.* Dedekind's *Essays on Number*, p. 48.

[†] If an aggregate B is contained in A, and E is the aggregate left when B is taken from A, we write

$$E \equiv A - B.$$

$P^{(a)}$, where a is any one of the "definitely defined symbols of infinity (*bestimmt definirte Unendlichkeitssymbole*)," is enumerable, then P is.

If the aggregates P_1, P_2, . . . have, two by two, no common point, for the aggregate P formed by the union of these (the "*Vereinigungsmenge*") Cantor now used the notation

$$P \equiv P_1 + P_2 + \dots$$

Now, we have the following identity

$$P' \equiv (P' - P'') + (P'' - P''') + \dots + (P^{(\nu-1)} - P^{(\nu)}) + P^{(\nu)};$$

and thus, since

$$P' - P'', \ P'' - P''', \ \dots, \ P^{(\nu-1)} - P^{(\nu)}$$

are all isolated and therefore enumerable, if $P^{(\nu)}$ is enumerable, then P' is also.

Now, suppose that $P^{(\infty)}$ exists; then, if any particular point of P' does not belong to $P^{(\infty)}$, there is a first one among the derivatives of finite order, $P^{(\nu)}$, to which it does not belong, and consequently $P^{(\nu-1)}$ contains it as an isolated point.   Thus we can write

$$P' \equiv (P' - P'') + (P'' - P''') + \dots + (P^{(\nu-1)} - P^{(\nu)})$$
$$+ \dots + P^{(\infty)};$$

and consequently, since an enumerable aggregate of enumerable aggregates is an enumerable aggregate of the elements of the latter, and $P^{(\infty)}$ is enumerable, then P' is also.   This can evidently be extended to $P^{(a)}$, if it exists, provided that the aggregate of all the derivatives from P' to $P^{(a)}$ is enumerable.

The considerations which arise from the last

observation appear to me to have constituted the final reason for considering these definitely infinite indices independently * on account of their connexion with the conception of "power," which Cantor had always regarded as the most fundamental one in the whole theory of aggregates. The series of the indices found, namely, is such that, up to any point (infinity or beyond), the aggregate of them is always enumerable, and yet a process exactly analogous to that used in the proof that the continuum is not enumerable leads to the result that the aggregate of all the indices such that, if α is any index, the aggregate of all the indices preceding α is enumerable, is not enumerable, but is, just as the power of the series of positive integers is the next higher one to all finite ones, the *next* greater infinite power to the first. And we can again imagine a new index which is the first after all those defined, just as after all the finite ones. We shall see these thoughts published by Cantor at the end of 1882.

It remains to mention the sixth theorem, in which Cantor proved that, if P' is enumerable, P has the property, which is essential in the theory of integration, of being "discrete," as Harnack called it, "integrable," as P. du Bois-Reymond did, "unextended," or, as it is now generally called, "content-less."

* When considered independently of P, these indices form a series beginning with the finite numbers, but extending beyond them ; so that it suggests itself that those other indices be considered as infinite (or transfinite) *numbers.*

VII

We have thus seen the importance of Cantor's "definitely defined symbols of infinity" in the theorem that if $P^{(a)}$ vanishes, P', and therefore P, is enumerable. This theorem may, as we can easily see by what precedes, be inverted as follows: If P' is enumerable, there is an index a such that $P^{(a)}$ vanishes. By defining these indices in an independent manner as real, and in general transfinite, integers, Cantor was enabled to form a conception of the enumeral * (*Anzahl*) of certain infinite series, and such series gave a means of defining a series of ascending infinite "powers." The conceptions of "enumeral" and "power" coincided in the case of finite aggregates, but diverged in the case of infinite aggregates; but this extension of the conception of enumeral served, in the way just mentioned, to develop and make precise the conception of power used often already.

Thus, from the new point of view gained, we get new insight into the theory of *finite* number; as Cantor put it: "The conception of number which, *in finito*, has only the background of enumeral, splits, in a manner of speaking, when we raise ourselves to the infinite, into the two conceptions of *power* . . . and *enumeral* . . . ; and, when I again descend to the finite, I see just as clearly and beautifully how these two conceptions again *unite* to form that of the finite integer."

---

* I have invented this word to translate " *Anzahl*," to avoid confusion with the word " number " (*Zahl*).

The significance of this distinction for the **theory** of all (finite and infinite) arithmetic appears in Cantor's own work * and, above all, in the later work of Russell.

Without this extension of the conception of number to the definitely infinite numbers, said Cantor, "it would hardly be possible for me to make without constraint the least step forwards in the theory of aggregates," and, although "I was led to them [these numbers] many years ago, without arriving at a clear consciousness that I possessed in them concrete numbers of real significance," yet "I was logically forced, almost against my will, because in opposition to traditions which had become valued by me in the course of scientific researches extending over many years, to the thought of considering the infinitely great, not merely in the form of the unlimitedly increasing, and in the form, closely connected with this, of convergent infinite series, but also to fix it mathematically by numbers in the definite form of a completed infinite.' I do not believe, then, that any reasons can be urged against it which I am unable to combat."

The indices of the series of the derivatives can be conceived as the series of finite numbers 1, 2, ..., followed by a series of *transfinite numbers* of which the first had been denoted by the symbol "∞." Thus, although there is no greatest

* *Cf.*, for example, pp. 113, 158–159 of the translations of Cantor's memoirs of 1895 and 1897 given below.

finite number, or, in other words, the supposition that there is a greatest finite number leads to contradiction, there is no contradiction involved in postulating a new, non-finite, number which is to be the *first after* all the finite numbers. This is the method adopted by Cantor * to define his numbers independently of the theory of derivatives ; we shall see how Cantor met any possible objections to this system of postulation.

Let us now briefly consider again the meaning of the word " *Mannichfaltigkeitslehre*," † which is usually translated as " theory of aggregates." In a note to the *Grundlagen*, Cantor remarked that he meant by this word " a doctrine embracing very much, which hitherto I have attempted to develop only in the special form of an arithmetical or geometrical theory of aggregates (*Mengenlehre*). By a manifold or aggregate I understand generally any multiplicity which can be thought of as one (*jedes Viele, welches sich als Eines denken lasst*), that is to say, any totality of definite elements which can be bound up into a whole by means of a law."

* " Ueber unendliche, lineare Punktmannichfaltigkeiten. V." [December 1882], *Math. Ann.*, vol. xxi, 1883, pp. 545-591 ; reprinted, with an added preface, with the title : *Grundlagen einer allgemeinen Mannichfaltigkeitslehre. Ein mathematisch-philosophischer Versuch in der Lehre des Unendlichen*, Leipzig, 1883 (page *n* of the *Grundlagen* is page *n* + 544 of the article in the *Math. Ann.*). This separate publication, with a title corresponding more nearly to its contents, was made " since it carries the subject in many respects much farther and thus is, for the most part, independent of the earlier essays " (Preface). In *Acta Math.*, ii, pp. 381-408, part of the *Grundlagen* was translated into French.

† Or " *Mannigfaltigkeitslehre*," or, more usually," *Mengenlehre* " ; in French, " *théorie des ensembles*." The English " theory of manifolds " has not come into general usage.

This character of unity was repeatedly emphasized by Cantor, as we shall see later.

The above quotations about the slow and sure way in which the transfinite numbers forced themselves on the mind of Cantor and about Cantor's philosophical and mathematical traditions are taken from the *Grundlagen*. Both here and in Cantor's later works we constantly come across discussions of opinions on infinity held by mathematicians and philosophers of all times, and besides such names as Aristotle, Descartes, Spinoza, Hobbes, Berkeley, Locke, Leibniz, Bolzano, and many others, we find evidence of deep erudition and painstaking search after new views on infinity to analyze. Cantor has devoted many pages to the Schoolmen and the Fathers of the Church.

The *Grundlagen* begins by drawing a distinction between two meanings which the word "infinity" may have in mathematics. The mathematical infinite, says Cantor, appears in two forms: Firstly, as an *improper* infinite (*Uneigentlich-Unendliches*), a magnitude which either increases above all limits or decreases to an arbitrary smallness, but always remains finite; so that it may be called a *variable finite*. Secondly, as a definite, a *proper* infinite (*Eigentlich-Unendliches*), represented by certain conceptions in geometry, and, in the theory of functions, by the point infinity of the complex plane. In the last case we have a single, definite point, and the behaviour of (analytic) functions about this point is examined in exactly the same way as it is

about any other point.* Cantor's infinite real
integers are also properly infinite, and, to emphasize
this, the old symbol " ∞ ," which was and is used also
for the improper infinite, was here replaced by "*ω*."

To define his new numbers, Cantor employed the
following considerations. The series of the real
positive integers,

(I)   1, 2, 3, . . ., *ν*, . . .,

arises from the repeated positing and uniting of
units which are presupposed and regarded as equal;
the number *ν* is the expression both for a definite
finite enumeral of such successive positings and for
the uniting of the posited units into a whole. Thus
the formation of the finite real integers rests on the
principle of the addition of a unit to a number
which has already been formed; Cantor called this
moment the *first principle of generation* (*Erzeugungs-
princip*). The enumeral of the number of the class
(I) so formed is infinite, and there is no greatest
among them. Thus, although it would be contradictory to speak of a greatest number of the class (I),
there is, on the other hand, nothing objectionable
in imagining a *new* number, *ω*, which is to express
that the whole collection (I) is given by its law in
its natural order of succession (in the same way as
ν is the expression that a certain finite enumeral of
units is united to a whole).† By allowing further

---

* "The behaviour of the function in the neighbourhood of the
infinitely distant point shows exactly the same occurrences as in that
of any other point lying *in finito*, so that hence it is completely justified
to think of the infinite, in this case, as situated in a point."

† "It is even permissible to think of the newly and created number

positings of unity to follow the positing of the number ω, we obtain with the help of the first principle of generation the further numbers :

$$\omega + 1, \quad \omega + 2, \quad \ldots, \quad \omega + \nu, \quad \ldots$$

Since again here we come to no greatest number, we imagine a new one, which we may call 2ω, and which is to be the first which follows all the numbers ν and $\omega + \nu$ hitherto formed. Applying the first principle repeatedly to the number 2ω, we come to the numbers :

$$2\omega + 1, \quad 2\omega + 2, \quad \ldots, \quad 2\omega + \nu, \quad \ldots$$

The logical function which has given us the numbers ω and 2ω is obviously different from the first principle ; Cantor called it the *second principle of generation* of real integers, and defined it more closely as follows : If there is defined any definite succession of real integers, of which there is no greatest, on the basis of this second principle a new number is created, which is defined as the next greater number to them all.

By the combined application of both principles we get, successively, the numbers :

$$3\omega, \; 3\omega + 1, \ldots, \; 3\omega + \nu, \ldots, \; \ldots, \; \mu\omega, \ldots, \; \mu\omega + \nu, \ldots$$

ω as the *limit* to which the numbers ν strive, if by that nothing else is understood than that ω is to be the first integer which follows all the numbers ν, that is to say, is to be called greater than every ν." *Cf.* the next section.

If we do not know the reasons in the theory of derivatives which prompted the introduction of ω, but only the grounds stated in the text for this introduction, it naturally seems rather arbitrary (not apparently, useful) to create ω because of the mere fact that it can apparently be defined in a manner free from contradiction. Thus, Cantor discussed (see below) such introductions or creations, found in them the distinguishing mark of pure mathematics, and justified them on historical grounds (on logical grounds they perhaps seem to need no justification).

and, since no number $\mu\omega+\nu$ is greatest, we create a new next number to all these, which may be denoted by ω^2. To this follow, in succession, numbers :

$$\lambda\omega^2+\mu\omega+\nu,$$

and further, we come to numbers of the form

$$\nu_0\omega^\mu+\nu_1\omega^{\mu-1}+ \ldots +\nu_{\mu-1}\omega+\nu_\mu;$$

and the second principle then requires a new number, which may conveniently be denoted by

$$\omega^\omega.$$

And so on indefinitely.

Now, it is seen without difficulty that the aggregate of all the numbers preceding any of the infinite numbers and hitherto defined is of the power of the first number-class (I). Thus, all the numbers preceding ω^ω are contained in the formula :

$$\nu_0\omega^\mu+\nu_1\omega^{\mu-1}+ \ldots +\nu_{\mu-1}+\omega+\nu_\mu;$$

where μ, ν_0, ν_1, $\ldots$, ν_μ have to take all finite, positive, integral values including zero and excluding the combination $\nu_\sigma=\nu_1= \ldots =\nu_\mu=0$. As is well known, this aggregate can be brought into the form of a simply infinite series, and has, therefore, the power of (I). Since, further, every sequence (itself of the first power) of aggregates, each of which has the first power, gives an aggregate of the first power, it is clear that we obtain, by the continuation of our sequence in the above way, only such numbers with which this condition is fulfilled.

Cantor defined the totality of all the numbers a formed by the help of the two principles

(II) $\quad \omega,\ \omega+1,\ \ldots,\ \nu_0\omega^\mu+\nu_1\omega^{\mu-1}+\ \ldots\ +\nu_{\mu-1}{}^{\omega+\nu}\mu,$
$$\ldots,\ \omega^\omega,\ \ldots,\ a,\ \ldots,$$

such that all the numbers, from 1 on, preceding a form an aggregate of the power of the first number-class (I), as the "*second number-class* (II)." The power of (II) is different from that of (I), and is, indeed, the *next higher* power, so that no other power lies between them. Accordingly, the second principle demands the creation of a new number (Ω) which follows all the numbers of (II) and is the first of the third number-class (III), and so on.*

Thus, in spite of first appearances, a certain completion can be given to the successive formation of the numbers of (II) which is similar to that limitation present with (I). There we only used the first principle, and so it was impossible to emerge from the series (I); but the *second* principle must lead not only over (II), but show itself indeed as a means, which, in combination with the first principle, gives the capacity to break through *every* limit in the formation of real integers. The above-mentioned requirement, that all the numbers to be next formed should be such that the aggregate

---

* It is particularly to be noticed that the second principle will take us *beyond any* class, and is not merely adequate to form numbers which are the limit-numbers of some *enumerable* series (so that a "third principle" is required to form Ω). The first and second principles together form *all* the numbers considered, while the "principle of limitation" enables us to define the various number-classes, of unbrokenly ascending powers in the series of these numbers.

of numbers preceding each one should be of a certain power, was called by Cantor the third or *limitation-principle* (*Hemmungs- oder Beschränkungsprincip*),* and which acts in such a manner that the class (II) defined with its aid can be shown to have a higher power than (I) and indeed the next higher power to it. In fact, the two first principles together define an absolutely infinite sequence of integers, while the third principle lays successively certain limits on this process, so that we obtain natural segments (*Abschnitte*), called number-classes, in this sequence.

Cantor's older (1873, 1878) conception of the "power" of an aggregate was, by this, developed and given precision. With finite aggregates the power coincides with the enumeral of the elements, for such aggregates have the same enumeral of elements in every order. With infinite aggregates, on the other hand, the transfinite numbers afford a means of defining the enumeral of an aggregate, if it be "well ordered," and the enumeral of such an aggregate of given power varies, in general, with the order given to the elements. The smallest infinite power is evidently that of (I), and, now for the first time, the successive higher powers also receive natural and simple definitions ; in fact, the power of the γth number class is the γth.

By a "well-ordered" aggregate,† Cantor under-

* "This principle (or requirement, or condition) circumscribes (*limits*) each number-class."

† The origin of this conception can easily be seen to be the defining of such aggregates as can be "enumerated" (using the word in the wider sense of Cantor, given below) by the transfinite numbers. In fact, the above definition of a well-ordered aggregate simply indicates

..n-defined aggregate whose elements h........ven definite succession such that there is a j...st element, a definite element follows every one (if it is not the last), and to any finite or infinite aggregate a definite element belongs which is the *next* following element in the succession to them all (unless there are no following elements in the succession). Two well-ordered aggregates are, now, of the same enumeral (with reference to the orders of succession of their elements previously given for them) if a one-to-one correspondence is possible between them such that, if E and F are any two different elements of the one, and E′ and F′ the corresponding elements (consequently different) of the other, if E precedes or follows F, then E′ respectively precedes or follows F′. This ordinal correspondence is evidently quite determinate, if it is possible at all, and since there is, in the extended number-series, one and only one number a such that its preceding numbers (from 1 on) in the natural succession have the same enumeral, we must put a for the enumeral of both well-ordered aggregates, if a is infinite, or $a-1$ if a is finite.

The essential difference between finite and infinite aggregates is, now, seen to be that a finite aggregate has the same enumeral whatever the succession of

the construction of any aggregate of the class required when the first two principles are used, but to generate elements, not numbers.

An important property of a well-ordered aggregate,—indeed, a characteristic property,—is that *any* series of terms in it, $a_1, a_2, \ldots, a_\nu, \ldots$, where $a_{\nu+1}$ precedes a_ν, must be finite. Even if the well-ordered aggregate in question is infinite, such a series as that described can never be *infinite*.

the elements may be, but an infinite aggregate has, in general, different enumerals under these circumstances. However, there is a certain connexion between enumeral and power—an attribute of the aggregate which is independent of the order of the elements. Thus, the enumeral of any well-ordered aggregate of the first power is a definite number of the second class, and every aggregate of the first power can always be put in such an order that its enumeral is any prescribed number of the second class. Cantor expressed this by extending the meaning of the word "enumerable" and saying: Every aggregate of the power of the first class is enumerable by numbers of the second class and only by these, and the aggregate can always be so ordered that it is *enumerated by* any prescribed number of the second class ; and analogously for the higher classes.

From his above remarks on the "absolute"*

---

* Cantor said "that, in the successive formation of number-classes, we can always go farther, and never reach a limit that cannot be surpassed,—so that we never reach an even approximate comprehension (*Erfassen*) of the Absolute,—I cannot doubt. The Absolute can only be recognized (*anerkannt*), but never apprehended (*erkannt*), even approximately. For just as inside the first number-class, at any finite number, however great, we always have the same 'power' of greater finite numbers before us, there follows any transfinite number of any one of the higher number-classes an aggregate of numbers and classes which has not in the least lost in 'power' in comparison with the whole absolutely infinite aggregate of numbers, from 1 on. The state of things is like that described by Albrecht von Haller : 'ich zieh' sie ab [die ungeheure Zahl] und Du [die Ewigkeit] liegst ganz vor mir.' The absolutely infinite sequence of numbers thus seems to me to be, in a certain sense, a suitable symbol of the Absolute ; whereas the infinity of (I), which has hitherto served for that purpose, appears to me, just because I hold it to be an idea (not presentation) that can be apprehended as a vanishing nothing in comparison with the former. It also seems to me remarkable that every number-class—and therefore every

infinity of the series of ordinal numbers and that of powers, it was to be expected that Cantor would derive the idea that *any* aggregate could be arranged in a well-ordered series, and this he stated with a promise to return to the subject later.*

The addition and multiplication of the transfinite (including the finite) numbers was thus defined by Cantor. Let M and M_1 be well-ordered aggregates of enumerals α and β, the aggregate which arises when first M is posited and then M_1, following it, and the two are united is denoted $M + M_1$ and its enumeral is defined to be $\alpha + \beta$. Evidently, if α and β are not both finite, $\alpha + \beta$ is, in general, different from $\beta + \alpha$. It is easy to extend the concept of sum to a finite or transfinite aggregate of summands in a definite order, and the associative law remains valid. Thus, in particular,

$$\alpha + (\beta + \gamma) = (\alpha + \beta) + \gamma.$$

If we take a succession (of enumeral β) of equal and similarly ordered aggregates, of which each is of enumeral α, we get a new well-ordered aggregate, whose enumeral is defined to be the product $\beta\alpha$,

power—corresponds to a definite number of the absolutely infinite totality of numbers, and indeed reciprocally, so that corresponding to any transfinite number γ there is a (γth) power ; so that the various powers also form an absolutely infinite sequence. This is so much the more remarkable as the number γ which gives the rank of a power (provided that γ has an immediate predecessor) stands, to the numbers of that number-class which has this power, in a magnitude-relation whose smallness mocks all description,—and this the more γ is taken to be greater."

* With this is connected the promise to prove later that the power of the continuum is that of (II), as stated, of course in other words, in 1878. See the Notes at the end of this book.

where β is the multiplier and α the multiplicand. Here also $\beta\alpha$ is, in general, different from $\alpha\beta$; but we have, in general,

$$\alpha(\beta\gamma) = (\alpha\beta)\gamma.$$

Cantor also promised an investigation of the "prime number-property" of some of the transfinite numbers * a proof of the non-existence of infinitely small numbers,† and a proof that his previous theorem on a point-aggregate P in an n-dimensional domain that, if the derivate $P^{(\alpha)}$, where α is any integer of (I) or (II), vanishes, P′, and hence P, is of the first power, can be thus inverted: If P is such a point-aggregate that P′ is of the first power, there is an integer α of (1) or (II) such that $P^{(\alpha)} = 0$, and there is a smallest of such α's. This last theorem shows the importance of the transfinite numbers in the theory of point-aggregates.

Cantor's proof that the power of (II) is different from that of (I) is analogous to his proof of the non-enumerability of the continuum. Suppose that we could put (II) in the form of a simple series:

$$(7) \qquad a_1, a_2, \ldots, a_\nu, \ldots,$$

we shall define a number which has the properties both of belonging to (II) and of not being a member of the series (7); and, since these properties are contradictory of one another if the hypothesis be granted, we must conclude that (II) cannot be put

---

* The property in question is: A "prime-number" α is such that the resolution $\alpha = \beta\gamma$ is only possible when $\beta = 1$ or $\beta = \alpha$.

† See the next section.

in the form (7), and therefore has not the power of
(I). Let a_{κ_2} be the first number of (1) which is
greater than a_1, a_{κ_3} the first greater than a_{κ_2}, and
so on ; so that we have

$$1 < \kappa_2 < \kappa_3 < \ldots$$

and

$$a_1 < a_{\kappa_2} < a_{\kappa_3} < \ldots ,$$

and

$$a_\nu < a_{\kappa_\lambda} \text{ if } \nu < \kappa_\lambda.$$

Now it may happen that, from a certain number
a_{κ_ρ} on, all following it in the series (7) are smaller
than it ; then it is evidently the greatest. If, on
the other hand, there is no such greatest number,
imagine the series of integers from 1 on and smaller
than a_1, add to it the series of integers $\geq a_1$ and
$> a_{\kappa_2}$, then the series of integers $\geq a_{\kappa_2}$ and $< a_{\kappa_3}$, and
so on ; we thus get a definite part of successive
numbers of (I) and (II) which is evidently of the
first power, and consequently, by the definition of
(II), there is a least number β of (II) which is
greater than all of these numbers. Therefore $\beta > a_{\kappa_\lambda}$
and thus also $\beta > a_\nu$, and also every number $\beta' < \beta$
is surpassed in magnitude by certain numbers a_{κ_λ}.

If there is a greatest $a_{\kappa_\rho} = \gamma$, then the number $\gamma + 1$
is a member of (II) and not of (7) ; and if there is
not a greatest, the number β is a member of (II)
and not of (7).

Further, the power of (II) is the *next greater* to
that of (I), so that no other powers lie between

them, for any aggregate of numbers of (I) and (II) is of the power of (I) or (II). In fact, this aggregate Z_1, when arranged in order of magnitude, is well-ordered, and may be represented by

$$(a_\beta), \quad (\beta = \omega, \ \omega + 1, \ \ldots \ a, \ \ldots)$$

where we always have $\beta < \Omega$, where Ω is the first number of (III); and consequently (a_β) is either finite or of the power of (I) or of that of (II), *quartum non datur.* From this results the theorem : If N is any well-defined aggregate of the second power, M′ is a part of M and M″ is a part of M′, and we know that M″ is of the same power as M, then M′ is of the same power as M, and therefore as M″; and Cantor remarked that this theorem is generally valid, and promised to return to it.[*]

Though the commutative law does not, in general, hold with the transfinite numbers, the associative law does, but the distributive law is only generally valid in the form :

$$(a + \beta)\gamma = a\gamma + \beta\gamma,$$

where $a + \beta$, a, and β are multipliers, "as we immediately recognize by inner intuition."

The subtraction, division, prime numbers, and addition and multiplication of numbers which can be put in the form of a rational and integral function of ω of the transfinite numbers were then dealt with

---

[*] From the occurrence of this theorem on p. 484 of the *Math. Ann.*, xlvi, 1895, which we now know (see the note on p. 204 below) to have been a forestalling of the theorem that any aggregate can be well-ordered, we may conclude that this latter theorem was used in this instance.

much in the same way as in the memoir of 1897 translated below. In the later memoir the subject is treated far more completely, and was drawn up with far more attention to logical form than was the *Grundlagen*.

An interesting part of the *Grundlagen* is the discussion of the conditions under which we are to regard the introduction into mathematics of a new conception, such as ω, as justified. The result of this discussion was already indicated by the way in which Cantor defined his new numbers : "We may regard the whole numbers as 'actual' in so far as they, on the ground of definitions, take a perfectly determined place in our understanding, are clearly distinguished from all other constituents of our thought, stand in definite relations to them, and thus modify, in a definite way, the substance of our mind." We may ascribe "actuality" to them "in so far as they must be held to be an expression or an image (*Abbild*) of processes and relations in the outer world, as distinguished from the intellect." Cantor's position was, now, that while there is no doubt that the first kind of reality always implies the second,* the proof of this is often a most difficult metaphysical problem ; but, in pure mathematics, we need only consider the first kind of reality, and consequently "mathematics is, in its development, quite free, and only subject to the

---

* This, according to Cantor, is a consequence of "the unity of the All, to which we ourselves belong," and so, in *pure* mathematics, we need only pay attention to the reality of our conceptions in the first sense, as stated in the text.

self-evident condition that its conceptions are **both free** from contradiction in themselves and stand in fixed relations, arranged by definitions, to previously formed and tested conceptions. In particular, in the introduction of new numbers, it is only obligatory to give such definitions of them as will afford them such a definiteness, and, under certain circumstances, such a relation to the older numbers, as permits them to be distinguished from one another in given cases. As soon as a number satisfies all these conditions, it can and must be considered as existent and real in mathematics. In this I see the grounds on which we must regard the rational, irrational, and complex numbers as just as existent as the positive integers."

There is no danger to be feared for science from this freedom in the formation of numbers, for, on the one hand, the conditions referred to under which this freedom can alone be exercised are such that they leave only a very small opportunity for arbitrariness ; and, on the other hand, every mathematical conception has in itself the necessary corrective,—if it is unfruitful or inconvenient, it shows this very soon by its unusability, and is then abandoned.

To support the idea that conceptions in pure mathematics are free, and not subject to any metaphysical control, Cantor quoted the names of, and the branches of mathematics founded by, some of the greatest mathematicians of the nineteenth century, among which an especially instructive example in Kummer's introduction of his "ideal" numbers into the theory of numbers. But "applied" mathematics, such as analytical mechanics and physics, is *metaphysical* both in its foundations and in its ends. "If it seeks to free itself of this, as was proposed lately by a celebrated physicist,* it degenerates into a 'describing of nature,' which must lack both the fresh breeze of free mathematical thought and the power of *explanation* and *grounding* of natural appearances."

The note of Cantor's on the process followed in the correct formation of conceptions is interesting. In his judgment, this process is everywhere the same ; we posit a thing without properties, which is at first nothing else than a name or a sign A, and give it in order different, even infinitely many, predicates, whose meaning for ideas already present is known, and which may not contradict one another. By this the relations of A to the conception already present, and in particular to the allied ones, are determined ; when we have completed this, all the conditions for the awakening of the conception A, which slumbers in us, are present, and it enters completed into "existence" in the first sense ; to prove its "existence" in the second sense is then a matter of metaphysics.

This seems to support the process by which Heine,

---

* This is evidently Kirchhoff. As is well known, Kirchhoff proposed (*Vorlesungen über mathematische Physik*, vol. i, Mechanik, Leipzig, 1874) this. *Cf.* E. Mach in his prefaces to his *Mechanics* (3rd ed., Chicago and London, 1907 ; Supplementary Volume, Chicago and London, 1915), and *Popular Scientific Lectures*, 3rd ed., Chicago and London, 1898, pp. 236–258.

in a paper partly inspired by his discussions with Cantor, defined the real numbers as *signs*, to which subsequently various properties were given.   But Cantor himself, as we shall see later, afterwards pointed out emphatically the mistake into which Kronecker and von Helmholtz fell when they started in their expositions of the number-concept with the last and most unessential thing—the ordinal *words* or *signs*—in the scientific theory of number ; so that we must, I think, regard this note of Cantor's as an indication that, at this time (1882), he was a supporter of the formalist theory of number,—or at least of rational and real non-integral numbers.

In fact, Cantor's notions as to what is meant by "existence" in mathematics—notions which are intimately connected with his introduction of irrational and transfinite numbers—were in substance identical with those of Hankel (1867) on "possible or impossible numbers."   Hankel was a formalist, though not a consistent one, and his theory was criticized with great acuteness by Frege in 1884. But these criticisms mark the beginning of the *logical* theory of mathematics, Cantor's earlier work belonging to the *formal* stage, and his later work to what may be called the *psychological* stage.

Finally, Cantor gave a discussion and exact determination of the meaning of the conception of "continuum."   After briefly referring to the discussions of this concept due to Leucippus, Democritus, Aristotle, Epicurus, Lucretius, and Thomas Aquinas, and emphasizing that we cannot begin, in this determination, with the conception of time or that of space, for these conceptions can only be clearly explained by means of a continuity-conception which must, of course, be independent of them, he started from the *n*-dimensional plane *arithmetical* space G_n, that is to say, the totality of systems of values

$$(x_1, \ x_2, \ \ldots, \ x_n),$$

in which every x can receive any real value from $-\infty$ to $+\infty$ independently of the others. Every such system is called an "arithmetical point" of G_n, the "distance" of two such points is defined by the expression

$$+ \sqrt{\{(x'_1 - x_1)^2 + (x'_2 - x_2)^2 + \ldots + (x'_n - x_n)^2\}},$$

and by an "arithmetical point-aggregate" P contained in G_n is meant any aggregate of points G_n selected out of it by a law. Thus the investigation comes to the establishment of a sharp and as general as possible a definition which should allow us to decide when P is to be called a "continuum."

If the first derivative P' is of the power of (I), there is a first number a of (I) or (II) for which $P^{(a)}$ vanishes; but if P' is not of the power of (I), P' can be always, and in only one way, divided into two aggregates R and S, where R is "reducible," —that is to say, such that there is a first number γ of (I) or (II) such that

$$R^{(\gamma)} \equiv o, —$$

and S is such that derivation does not alter it.   Then

$$S \equiv S'$$

and consequently also

$$S \equiv S^{(\gamma)},$$

and S is said to be "perfect."   No aggregate can
be both reducible and perfect, "but, on the other
hand, irreducible. is not so much as perfect, nor
imperfect exactly the same as reducible, as we
easily see with some attention."

Perfect aggregates are by no means always everywhere dense ; an example of such an aggregate
which is everywhere dense in *no* interval was given
by Cantor.   Thus such aggregates are not fitted
for the complete definition of a continuum, although
we must grant that the continuum must be perfect.
The other predicate is that the aggregate must be
connected (*zusammenhängend*), that is to say, if t
and t' are any two of its points and ϵ a given arbitrarily small positive number, a finite number of
points t_1, t_2, . . ., t_ν of P exist such that the distances tt_1, $t_1 t_2$, . . ., $t_\nu t'$ are all less than ϵ.

"All the geometric point-continua known to us
are, as is easy to see, connected ; and I believe,
now, that I recognize in these two predicates
'perfect' and 'connected' the necessary and sufficient
characteristics of a point-continuum."

Bolzano's (1851) definition of a continuum is
certainly not correct, for it expresses only *one*
property of a continuum, which is also possessed by

aggregates which arise from G_n when any isolated aggregate is removed from it, and also in those consisting of many separated continua. Also Dedekind * appeared to Cantor only to emphasize *another* property of a continuum, namely, that which it has in common with all other perfect aggregates.

We will pass over the development of the theory of point-aggregates subsequently to 1882—Bendixson's and Cantor's researches on the power of perfect aggregates, Cantor's theory of "adherences" and "coherences," the investigations of Cantor, Stolz, Harnack, Jordan, Borel, and others on the "content" of aggregates, and the applications of the theory of point-aggregates to the theory of functions made by Jordan, Brodén, Osgood, Baire, Arzelà, Schoenflies, and many others,—and will now trace the development, in Cantor's hands, of the theory of the transfinite cardinal and ordinal numbers from 1883 to 1895.

VIII

An account of the development that the theory of transfinite numbers underwent in Cantor's mind from 1883 to 1890 is described in his articles published in the *Zeitschrift für Philosophie und philosophische Kritik* for 1887 and 1888, and collected and published in 1890 under the title *Zur Lehre vom Transfiniten*. A great part of this little book is taken up with detailed discussions about philosophers' denials of the possibility of infinite

* *Essays on Number*, p. 11.

numbers, extracts from letters to and from philosophers and theologians, and so on.* "All so-
called proofs of the impossibility of actually infinite
numbers," said Cantor, "are, as may be shown in
every particular case and also on general grounds,
false in that they begin by attributing to the
numbers in question all the properties of finite
numbers, whereas the infinite numbers, if they are
to be thinkable in any form, must constitute quite
a new kind of number as opposed to the finite
numbers, and the nature of this new kind of number
is dependent on the nature of things and is an object
of investigation, but not of our arbitrariness or our
prejudice."

In 1883 Cantor had begun to lecture on his view
of whole numbers and types of order as general
concepts or universals (*unum versus alia*) which
relate to aggregates and arise from these aggregates
when we abstract from the nature of the elements.
"Every aggregate of distinct things can be regarded
as a unitary thing in which the things first mentioned
are constitutive elements. If we abstract *both* from
the nature of the elements and from the order in
which they are given, we get the ' cardinal number '
or ' power ' of the aggregate, a general concept in
which the elements, as so-called units, have so
grown organically into one another to make a
unitary whole that no one of them ranks above the
others. Hence results that two different aggregates
have the same cardinal number when and only when

* *Cf.* § VII, near the beginning.

they are what I call 'equivalent' to one another, and there is no contradiction when, as often happens with infinite aggregates, two aggregates of which one is a part of the other have the same cardinal number. I regard the non-recognition of this fact as the principal obstacle to the introduction of infinite numbers. If the act of abstraction referred to, when we have to do with an aggregate ordered according to one or many relations (dimensions), is only performed with respect to the nature of the elements, so that the ordinal rank in which these elements stand to one another is kept in the general concept, the organic whole arising is what I call 'ordinal type,' or in the special case of well-ordered aggregates an 'ordinal number.' This ordinal number is the same thing that I called, in my *Grundlagen* of 1883, the 'enumeral (*Anzahl*) of a well-ordered aggregate.' Two ordered aggregates have one and the same ordinal type if they stand to one another in the relation of 'similarity,' which relation will be exactly defined. These are the roots from which develops with logical necessity the organism of transfinite theory of types and in particular of the transfinite ordinal numbers, and which I hope soon to publish in a systematic form."

The contents of a lecture given in 1883 were also given in a letter of 1884. In it was pointed out that the cardinal number of an aggregate M is the general concept under which fall all aggregates equivalent to M, and that :

"One of the most important problems of the

theory of aggregates, which I believe I have solved as to its principal part in my *Grundlagen*, consists in the question of determining the various powers of the aggregates in the whole of nature, in so far as we can know it.   This end I have reached by the development of the general concept of enumeral of well-ordered aggregates, or, what is the same thing, of the concept of ordinal number." The concept of ordinal number is a special case of the concept of ordinal type, which relates to any simply or multiply ordered aggregate in the same way as the ordinal number to a well-ordered aggregate. The problem here arises of determining the various ordinal numbers in nature.

When Cantor said that he had solved the chief part of the problem of determining the various powers in nature, he meant that he had almost proved that the power of the arithmetical continuum is the same as the power of the ordinal numbers of the second class.   In spite of the fact that Cantor firmly believed this, possibly on account of the fact that all known aggregates in the continuum had been found to be either of the first power or of the power of the continuum, the proof or disproof of this theorem has not even now been carried out, and there is some ground for believing that it cannot be carried out.

What Cantor, in his *Grundlagen*, had noted as the relation of two well-ordered aggregates which have the same enumeral was here called the relation of "similarity," and in the laws of multiplication of two ordinal numbers he departed from the custom followed in the *Grundlagen* and wrote the multiplier on the right and the multiplicand on the left. The importance of this alteration is seen by the fact that we can write : $a^\beta \cdot a^\gamma = a^{\beta+\gamma}$; whereas we would have to write, in the notation of the *Grundlagen* : $a^\beta \cdot a^\gamma = a^{\gamma+\beta}$.

At the end of this letter, Cantor remarked that ω may, in a sense, be regarded as the limit to which the variable finite whole number ν tends. Here " ω is the least transfinite ordinal number which is greater than *all* finite numbers ; exactly in the same way that $\sqrt{2}$ is the limit of certain variable, increasing, rational numbers, with this difference : the difference between $\sqrt{2}$ and these approximating fractions becomes as small as we wish, whereas $\omega - \nu$ is always equal to ω. But this difference in no way alters the fact that ω is to be regarded as as definite and completed as $\sqrt{2}$, and in no way alters the fact that ω has no more trace of the numbers ν which tend to it than $\sqrt{2}$ has of the approximating fractions. The transfinite numbers are in a sense *new irrationalities*, and indeed in my eyes the best method of defining *finite* irrational numbers is the same in principle as my method of introducing transfinite numbers. We can say that the transfinite numbers stand or fall with finite irrational numbers, in their inmost being they are alike, for both are definitely marked off modifications of the actually infinite."

With this is connected in principle an extract from

a letter written in 1886: "Finally I have still to explain to you in what sense I conceive the minimum of the transfinite as limit of the increasing finite. For this purpose we must consider that the concept of 'limit' in the domain of finite numbers has two essential characteristics. For example, the number 1 is the limit of the numbers $z_\nu = 1 - 1/\nu$, where ν is a variable, finite, whole number, which increases above all finite limits. In the first place the difference $1 - z_\nu$ is a magnitude which becomes infinitely small; in the second place 1 is the least of all numbers which are greater than all magnitudes z_ν. Each of these two properties characterizes the finite number 1 as limit of the variable magnitude z_ν. Now if we wish to extend the concept of limit to transfinite limits as well, the second of the above characteristics is used; the first must here be allowed to drop because it has a meaning only for finite limits. Accordingly I call ω the limit of the increasing, finite, whole numbers ν, because ω is the least of all numbers which are greater than all the finite numbers. But $\omega - \nu$ is always equal to ω, and therefore we cannot say that the increasing numbers ν come as near as we wish to ω; indeed any number ν however great is quite as far off from ω as the least finite number. Here we see especially clearly the very important fact that my least transfinite ordinal number ω, and consequently all greater ordinal numbers, lie quite outside the endless series 1, 2, 3, and so on. Thus ω is *not* a maximum of the finite numbers, for there is no such thing."

In another letter written in 1886, Cantor emphasized another aspect of irrational numbers. In all
of the definitions of these numbers there is used,
as is indeed essential, a special *actually infinite*
aggregate of rational numbers. In both this and
another letter of 1886, Cantor returned in great
detail to the distinction between the "potential"
and "actual" infinite of which he had made a great
point under other names in his *Grundlagen*. The
potential infinite is a variable finite, and in order
that such a variable may be completely known, we
must be able to determine the domain of variability,
and this domain can only be, in general, an actually
infinite aggregate of values. Thus every potential
infinite presupposes an actually infinite, and these
"domains of variability" which are studied in the
theory of aggregates are the foundations of arithmetic and analysis. Further, besides actually infinite
aggregates, we have to consider in mathematics
natural abstractions from these aggregates, which
form the material of the theory of transfinite
numbers.

In 1885, Cantor had developed to a large extent
his theory of cardinal numbers and ordinal types.

In the fairly long paper which he wrote out, he
laid particular stress on the theory of ordinal types
and entered into details which he had not published
before as to the definition of ordinal type in general,
of which ordinal number is a particular case. In
this paper also he denoted the cardinal number of
an aggregate M by $\overline{\overline{M}}$, and the ordinal type of

M by $\overline{M}$; thus indicating by lines over the letter that a double or single act of abstraction is to be performed.

In the theory of cardinal numbers, he defined the addition and multiplication of two cardinal numbers and proved the fundamental laws about them in much the same way as he did in the memoir of 1895 which is translated below. It is characteristic of Cantor's views that he distinguished very sharply between an aggregate and a cardinal number that belongs to it : "Is not an aggregate an object *outside* us, whereas its cardinal number is an abstract picture of it *in our* mind?"

In an ordered aggregate of any number of dimensions, such as the totality of points in space, as determined by three rectangular co-ordinates, or a piece of music whose dimensions are the sequence of the tones in time, the duration of each tone in time, the pitch of the tones, and the intensity of the tones, then "if we make abstraction of the nature of the elements, while we retain their rank in all the *n* different directions, an intellectual picture, a general concept, is generated in us, and I call this the *n*-ple ordinal type." The definition of the "similarity of ordered aggregates" is :

"Two *n*-ply ordered aggregates M and N are called similar if it is possible so to make their elements correspond to another uniquely and completely that, if E and E′ are any two elements of M and F and F′ the two corresponding elements of N, then for $\nu = 1, 2, \ldots n$ the relation of rank of

E to E' in the νth direction inside the aggregate M is exactly the same as the relation of rank of F to F' in the νth direction inside the aggregate N. We will call such a correspondence of two aggregates which are similar to one another an imaging of the one on the other."

The addition and multiplication of ordinal types, and the fundamental laws about them, were then dealt with much as in the memoir of 1895 which is translated below. The rest of the paper was devoted to a consideration of problems about n-ple finite types.

In 1888, Cantor, who had arrived at a very clear notion that the essential part of the concept of number lay in the unitary concept that we form, gave some interesting criticisms on the essays of Helmholtz and Kronecker, which appeared in 1887, on the concept of number. Both the authors referred to started with the last and most unessential feature in our treatment of ordinal numbers : the words or other signs that we use to represent these numbers.

In 1887, Cantor gave a more detailed proof of the non-existence of actually infinitely small magnitudes. This proof was referred to in advance in the *Grundlagen*, and was later put into a more rigorous form by Peano.

We have already referred to the researches of Cantor on point-aggregates published in 1883 and later ; the only other paper besides those already dealt with that was published by Cantor on an important question in the theory of transfinite numbers was one published in 1892. In this paper we can see the origins of the conception of "covering" (*Belegung*) defined in the memoir of 1895 translated below. In the terminology introduced in this memoir, we can say that the paper of 1892 contains a proof that 2, when exponentiated by a transfinite cardinal number, gives rise to a cardinal number which is greater than the cardinal number first mentioned.

The introduction of the concept of "covering" is the most striking advance in the principles of the theory of transfinite numbers from 1885 to 1895, and we can now study the final and considered form which Cantor gave to the theory in two important memoirs of 1895 and 1897. The principal advances in the theory since 1897 will be referred to in the notes at the end of this book.

CONTRIBUTIONS TO THE FOUNDING OF THE THEORY OF TRANSFINITE NUMBERS

CONTRIBUTIONS TO THE FOUNDING OF THE THEORY OF TRANSFINITE NUMBERS

(First Article)

"Hypotheses non fingo."

"Neque enim leges intellectui aut rebus damus ad arbitrium nostrum, sed tanquam scribæ fideles ab ipsius naturæ voce latas et prolatas excipimus et describimus."

"Veniet tempus, quo ista quæ nunc latent, in lucem dies extrahat et longioris ævi diligentia."

§ 1

The Conception of Power or Cardinal Number

By an "aggregate" (*Menge*) we are to understand any collection into a whole (*Zusammenfassung zu einem Ganzen*) M of definite and separate objects *m* of our intuition or our thought. These objects are called the "elements" of M.

In signs we express this thus :

(1)   M = {m}.

We denote the uniting of many aggregates M, N, P, . . ., which have no common elements, into a single aggregate by

(2)   (M, N, P, . . .).

The elements of this aggregate are, therefore, the elements of M, of N, of P, . . ., taken together.

We will call by the name "part" or "partial aggregate" of an aggregate M any other aggregate M_1 whose elements are also elements of M.

If M_2 is a part of M_1 and M_1 is a part of M, then M_2 is a part of M.

Every aggregate M has a definite "power," which we will also call its "cardinal number."

We will call by the name "power" or "cardinal number" of M the general concept which, by means of our active faculty of thought, arises from the aggregate M when we make abstraction of the nature of its various elements m and of the order in which they are given.

[482] We denote the result of this double act of abstraction, the cardinal number or power of M, by

(3) $\overline{\overline{M}}$.

Since every single element m, if we abstract from its nature, becomes a "unit," the cardinal number $\overline{\overline{M}}$ is a definite aggregate composed of units, and this number has existence in our mind as an intellectual image or projection of the given aggregate M.

We say that two aggregates M and N are "equivalent," in signs

(4) $M \backsim N$ or $N \backsim M$,

if it is possible to put them, by some law, in such a relation to one another that to every element of each one of them corresponds one and only one element of the other. To every part M_1 of M there corresponds, then, a definite equivalent part N_1 of N, and inversely.

If we have such a law of co-ordination of two equivalent aggregates, then, apart from the case when each of them consists only of one element, we can modify this law in many ways. We can, for instance, always take care that to a special element m_0 of M a special element n_0 of N corresponds. For if, according to the original law, the elements m_0 and n_0 do not correspond to one another, but to the element m_0 of M the element n_1 of N corresponds, and to the element n_0 of N the element m_1 of M corresponds, we take the modified law according to which m_0 corresponds to n_0 and m_1 to n_1 and for the other elements the original law remains unaltered. By this means the end is attained.

Every aggregate is equivalent to itself :

(5) $$M \backsim M.$$

If two aggregates are equivalent to a third, they are equivalent to one another ; that is to say :

(6) from $M \backsim P$ and $N \backsim P$ follows $M \backsim N$.

Of fundamental importance is the theorem that two aggregates M and N have the same cardinal number if, and only if, they are equivalent : thus,

(7)   from $M \backsim N$ we get $\overline{\overline{M}} = \overline{\overline{N}}$,
and

(8)   from $\overline{\overline{M}} = \overline{\overline{N}}$ we get $M \backsim N$.

Thus the equivalence of aggregates forms the necessary and sufficient condition for the equality of their cardinal numbers.

[483] In fact, according to the above-definition of power, the cardinal number $\overline{\overline{M}}$ remains unaltered if in the place of each of one or many or even all elements m of M other things are substituted. If, now, $M \backsim N$, there is a law of co-ordination by means of which M and N are uniquely and reciprocally referred to one another; and by it to the element m of M corresponds the element n of N. Then we can imagine, in the place of every element m of M, the corresponding element n of N substituted, and, in this way, M transforms into N without alteration of cardinal number.   Consequently

$$\overline{\overline{M}} = \overline{\overline{N}}.$$

The converse of the theorem results from the remark that between the elements of M and the different units of its cardinal number M a reciprocally univocal (or bi-univocal) relation of correspondence subsists.   For, as we saw, $\overline{\overline{M}}$ grows, so to speak, out of M in such a way that from every element m of M a special unit of M arises.   Thus we can say that

(9) $M \backsim \overline{\overline{M}}.$

In the same way $N \backsim \overline{\overline{N}}$.   If then $\overline{\overline{M}} = \overline{\overline{N}}$, we have, by (6), $M \backsim N$.

We will mention the following theorem, which results immediately from the conception of equivalence. If M, N, P, . . . are aggregates which have no common elements, M', N', P', . . . are also aggregates with the same property, and if

$$M \backsim M', \quad N \backsim N', \quad P \backsim P', \quad \ldots,$$

then we always have

$$(M, N, P, \ldots) \backsim (M', N', P', \ldots).$$

§ 2

"Greater" and "Less" with Powers

If for two aggregates M and N with the cardinal numbers $\mathfrak{a} = \overline{\overline{M}}$ and $\mathfrak{b} = \overline{\overline{N}}$, both the conditions :

(*a*) There is no part of M which is equivalent to N,

(*b*) There is a part N_1 of N, such that $N_1 \backsim M$,

are fulfilled, it is obvious that these conditions still hold if in them M and N are replaced by two equivalent aggregates M' and N'. Thus they express a definite relation of the cardinal numbers $\mathfrak{a}$ and $\mathfrak{b}$ to one another.

[484] Further, the equivalence of M and N, and thus the equality of $\mathfrak{a}$ and $\mathfrak{b}$, is excluded ; for if we had $M \backsim N$, we would have, because $N_1 \backsim M$, the equivalence $N_1 \backsim N$, and then, because $M \backsim N$, there would exist a part M_1 of M such that $M_1 \backsim M$, and therefore we should have $M_1 \backsim N$; and this contradicts the condition (*a*).

Thirdly, the relation of $\mathfrak{a}$ to $\mathfrak{b}$ is such that it makes impossible the same relation of $\mathfrak{b}$ to $\mathfrak{a}$; for if in (*a*) and (*b*) the parts played by M and N are interchanged, two conditions arise which are contradictory to the former ones.

We express the relation of $\mathfrak{a}$ to $\mathfrak{b}$ characterized by (*a*) and (*b*) by saying : $\mathfrak{a}$ is "less" than $\mathfrak{b}$ or $\mathfrak{b}$ is "greater" than $\mathfrak{a}$; in signs

(1) $$\mathfrak{a} < \mathfrak{b} \quad \text{or} \quad \mathfrak{b} > \mathfrak{a}.$$

We can easily prove that,

(2) if $\mathfrak{a} < \mathfrak{b}$ and $\mathfrak{b} < \mathfrak{c}$, then we always have $\mathfrak{a} < \mathfrak{c}$.

Similarly, from the definition, it follows at once that, if P_1 is part of an aggregate P, from $\mathfrak{a} < \overline{\overline{P}}_1$ follows $\mathfrak{a} < \overline{\overline{P}}$ and from $\overline{\overline{P}} < \mathfrak{b}$ follows $\overline{\overline{P}}_1 < \mathfrak{b}$.

We have seen that, of the three relations

$$\mathfrak{a} = \mathfrak{b}, \quad \mathfrak{a} < \mathfrak{b}, \quad \mathfrak{b} < \mathfrak{a},$$

each one excludes the two others. On the other hand, the theorem that, with any two cardinal numbers $\mathfrak{a}$ and $\mathfrak{b}$, one of those three relations must necessarily be realized, is by no means self-evident and can hardly be proved at this stage.

Not until later, when we shall have gained a survey over the ascending sequence of the transfinite cardinal numbers and an insight into their connexion, will result the truth of the theorem :

A. If $\mathfrak{a}$ and $\mathfrak{b}$ are any two cardinal numbers, then either $\mathfrak{a} = \mathfrak{b}$ or $\mathfrak{a} < \mathfrak{b}$ or $\mathfrak{a} > \mathfrak{b}$.

From this theorem the following theorems, of which, however, we will here make no use, can be very simply derived :

B. If two aggregates M and N are such that M is equivalent to a part N_1 of N and N to a part M_1 of M, then M and N are equivalent ;

C. If M_1 is a part of an aggregate M, M_2 is a part of the aggregate M_1, and if the aggregates M and M_2 are equivalent, then M_1 is equivalent to both M and M_2 ;

D. If, with two aggregates M and N, N is equivalent neither to M nor to a part of M, there is a part N_1 of N that is equivalent to M ;

E. If two aggregates M and N are not equivalent, and there is a part N_1 of N that is equivalent to M, then no part of M is equivalent to N.

[485] § 3
The Addition and Multiplication of Powers

The union of two aggregates M and N which have no common elements was denoted in § 1, (2), by (M, N). We call it the "union-aggregate (*Vereinigungsmenge*) of M and N."

If M' and N' are two other aggregates without common elements, and if M $\sim$ M' and N $\sim$ N', we saw that we have

$$(M, N) \sim (M', N').$$

Hence the cardinal number of (M, N) only depends upon the cardinal numbers $\overline{\overline{M}} = \mathfrak{a}$ and $\overline{\overline{N}} = \mathfrak{b}$.

This leads to the definition of the sum of $\mathfrak{a}$ and $\mathfrak{b}$. We put

(1) $\qquad \mathfrak{a} + \mathfrak{b} = (\overline{\overline{M, N}}).$

Since in the conception of power, we abstract from the order of the elements, we conclude at once that

(2) $$\mathfrak{a} + \mathfrak{b} = \mathfrak{b} + \mathfrak{a};$$

and, for any three cardinal numbers $\mathfrak{a}$, $\mathfrak{b}$, $\mathfrak{c}$, we have

(3) $$\mathfrak{a} + (\mathfrak{b} + \mathfrak{c}) = (\mathfrak{a} + \mathfrak{b}) + \mathfrak{c}.$$

We now come to multiplication. Any element m of an aggregate M can be thought to be bound up with any element n of another aggregate N so as to form a new element (m, n); we denote by (M.N) the aggregate of all these bindings (m, n), and call it the "aggregate of bindings (*Verbindungsmenge*) of M and N." Thus

(4) $$(M.N) = \{(m, n)\}.$$

We see that the power of (M.N) only depends on the powers $\overline{\overline{M}} = \mathfrak{a}$ and $\overline{\overline{N}} = \mathfrak{b}$; for, if we replace the aggregates M and N by the aggregates

$$M' = \{m'\} \quad \text{and} \quad N' = \{n'\}$$

respectively equivalent to them, and consider m, m' and n, n' as corresponding elements, then the aggregate

$$(M'.N') = \{(m', n')\}$$

is brought into a reciprocal and univocal correspondence with (M.N) by regarding (m, n) and (m', n') as corresponding elements. Thus

(5) $$(M'.N') \backsim (M.N).$$

We now define the product $\mathfrak{a}.\mathfrak{b}$ by the equation

(6) $$\mathfrak{a}.\mathfrak{b} = \overline{\overline{(M.N)}}.$$

[486] An aggregate with the cardinal number $a.b$ may also be made up out of two aggregates M and N with the cardinal numbers a and b according to the following rule : We start from the aggregate N and replace in it every element n by an aggregate $M_n \backsim M$; if, then, we collect the elements of all these aggregates M_n to a whole S, we see that

$$(7) \qquad\qquad S \backsim (M.N),$$

and consequently

$$\overline{\overline{S}} = a.b.$$

For, if, with any given law of correspondence of the two equivalent aggregates M and M_n, we denote by m the element of M which corresponds to the element m_n of M_n, we have

$$(8) \qquad\qquad S = \{m_n\};$$

and thus the aggregates S and (M.N) can be referred reciprocally and univocally to one another by regarding m_n and (m, n) as corresponding elements.

From our definitions result readily the theorems :

$$(9) \qquad\qquad a.b = b.a,$$
$$(10) \qquad\qquad a.(b.c) = (a.b).c,$$
$$(11) \qquad\qquad a(b+c) = ab+ac ;$$

because :

$$(M.N) \backsim (N.M),$$
$$\big(M.(N.P)\big) \backsim \big((M.N).P\big),$$
$$\big(M.(N,\ P)\big) \backsim \big((M.N),\ (M.P)\big).$$

Addition and multiplication of powers are subject,

therefore, to the commutative, associative, and distributive laws.

§ 4

The Exponentiation of Powers

By a "covering of the aggregate N with elements of the aggregate M," or, more simply, by a "covering of N with M," we understand a law by which with every element n of N a definite element of M is bound up, where one and the same element of M can come repeatedly into application. The element of M bound up with n is, in a way, a one-valued function of n, and may be denoted by $f(n)$; it is called a "covering function of n." The corresponding covering of N will be called $f(N)$.

[487] Two coverings $f_1(N)$ and $f_2(N)$ are said to be equal if, and only if, for all elements n of N the equation

$$(1) \qquad f_1(n) = f_2(n)$$

is fulfilled, so that if this equation does not subsist for even a single element $n = n_0$, $f_1(N)$ and $f_2(N)$ are characterized as different coverings of N. For example, if m_0 is a particular element of M, we may fix that, for all n's

$$f(n) = m_0;$$

this law constitutes a particular covering of N with M. Another kind of covering results if m_0 and m_1 are two different particular elements of M and n_0 a particular element of N, from fixing that

$$f(n_0) = m_0$$
$$f(n) = m_1,$$

for all n's which are different from n_0.

The totality of different coverings of N with M forms a definite aggregate with the elements $f(N)$; we call it the "covering-aggregate (*Belegungsmenge*) of N with M" and denote it by $(N \mid M)$. Thus:

$$(2) \qquad (N \mid M) = \{f(N)\}.$$

If $M \backsim M'$ and $N \backsim N'$, we easily find that

$$(3) \qquad (N \mid M) \backsim (N' \mid M').$$

Thus the cardinal number of $(N \mid M)$ depends only on the cardinal numbers $\overline{\overline{M}} = \mathfrak{a}$ and $\overline{\overline{N}} = \mathfrak{b}$; it serves us for the definition of $\mathfrak{a}^{\mathfrak{b}}$:

$$(4) \qquad \mathfrak{a}^{\mathfrak{b}} = \overline{\overline{(N \mid M)}}.$$

For any three aggregates, M, N, P, we easily prove the theorems:

$$(5) \qquad \big((N \mid M) . (P \mid M)\big) \backsim \big((N, P) \mid M\big),$$
$$(6) \qquad \big((P \mid M) . (P \mid N)\big) \backsim \big(P \mid (M . N)\big),$$
$$(7) \qquad \big(P \mid (N \mid M)\big) \backsim \big((P . N) \mid M\big),$$

from which, if we put $\overline{\overline{P}} = \mathfrak{c}$, we have, by (4) and by paying attention to § 3, the theorems for any three cardinal numbers, $\mathfrak{a}$, $\mathfrak{b}$, and $\mathfrak{c}$:

$$(8) \qquad \mathfrak{a}^{\mathfrak{b}} . \mathfrak{a}^{\mathfrak{c}} = \mathfrak{a}^{\mathfrak{b}+\mathfrak{c}},$$
$$(9) \qquad \mathfrak{a}^{\mathfrak{c}} . \mathfrak{b}^{\mathfrak{c}} = (\mathfrak{a} . \mathfrak{b})^{\mathfrak{c}},$$
$$(10) \qquad (\mathfrak{a}^{\mathfrak{b}})^{\mathfrak{c}} = \mathfrak{a}^{\mathfrak{b} . \mathfrak{c}}.$$

[488] We see how pregnant and far-reaching these simple formulæ extended to powers are by the following example.   If we denote the power of the linear continuum X (that is, the totality X of real numbers x such that $x \geq$ and ≤ 1) by $\mathfrak{o}$, we easily see that it may be represented by, amongst others, the formula :

$$(11) \qquad\qquad \mathfrak{o} = 2^{\aleph_0},$$

where § 6 gives the meaning of $\aleph_0$.   In fact, by (4), $2^{\aleph}$ is the power of all representations

$$(12) \qquad x = \frac{f(1)}{2} + \frac{f(2)}{2^2} + \ldots + \frac{f(\nu)}{2^\nu} + \ldots$$

$$\text{(where } f(\nu) = 0 \text{ or } 1)$$

of the numbers x in the binary system.   If we pay attention to the fact that every number x is only represented once, with the exception of the numbers $x = \dfrac{2\nu + 1}{2^\mu} < 1$, which are represented twice over, we have, if we denote the "enumerable" totality of the latter by $\{s_\nu\}$,

$$2^{\aleph_0} = \overline{\overline{(\{s_\nu\}, \; X)}}.$$

If we take away from X any "enumerable" aggregate $\{t_\nu\}$ and denote the remainder by X_1, we have :

$$X = (\{t_\nu\}, \; X_1) = (\{t_{2\nu-1}\}, \; \{t_{2\nu}\}, \; X_1),$$

$$(\{s_\nu\}, \; X) = (\{s_\nu\}, \; \{t_\nu\}, \; X_1),$$

$$\{t_{2\nu-1}\} \backsim \{s_\nu\}, \quad \{t_{2\nu}\} \backsim \{t_\nu\}, \quad X_1 \backsim X_1 \, ;$$

$$X \backsim (\{s_\nu\}, \; X),$$

and thus (§ 1)

$$2^{\aleph_0} = \overline{\overline{X}} = \mathfrak{o}.$$

From (11) follows by squaring (by § 6, (6))

$$\mathfrak{o} \cdot \mathfrak{o} = 2^{\aleph_0} \cdot 2^{\aleph_0} = 2^{\aleph_0 + \aleph_0} = 2^{\aleph_0} = \mathfrak{o},$$

and hence, by continued multiplication by $\mathfrak{o}$,

$$(13) \qquad\qquad \mathfrak{o}^\nu = \mathfrak{o},$$

where ν is any finite cardinal number.

If we raise both sides of (11) to the power * $\aleph_0$ we get

$$\mathfrak{o}^{\aleph_0} = (2^{\aleph_0})^{\aleph_0} = 2^{\aleph_0 \cdot \aleph_0}.$$

But since, by § 6, (8), $\aleph_0 \cdot \aleph_0 = \aleph_0$, we have

$$(14) \qquad\qquad \mathfrak{o}^{\aleph_0} = \mathfrak{o}.$$

The formulæ (13) and (14) mean that both the ν-dimensional and the $\aleph_0$-dimensional continuum have the power of the one-dimensional continuum. Thus the whole contents of my paper in Crelle's *Journal*, vol. lxxxiv, 1878,† are derived purely algebraically with these few strokes of the pen from the fundamental formulæ of the calculation with cardinal numbers.

[489] § 5

The Finite Cardinal Numbers

We will next show how the principles which we have laid down, and on which later on the theory of the actually infinite or transfinite cardinal numbers

* [In English there is an ambiguity.]
† [See Section V of the Introduction.]

will be built, afford also the most natural, shortest, and most rigorous foundation for the theory of finite numbers.

To a single thing e_0, if we subsume it under the concept of an aggregate $E_0 = (e_0)$, corresponds as cardinal number what we call "one" and denote by 1 ; we have

$$(1) \qquad\qquad 1 = \overline{\overline{E}}_0.$$

Let us now unite with E_0 another thing e_1, and call the union-aggregate E_1, so that

$$(2) \qquad E_1 = (E_0,\ e_1) = (e_0,\ e_1).$$

The cardinal number of E_1 is called "two" and is denoted by 2 :

$$(3) \qquad\qquad 2 = \overline{\overline{E}}_1.$$

By addition of new elements we get the series of aggregates

$$E_2 = (E_1,\ e_2), \quad E_3 = (E_2,\ e_3), \ldots,$$

which give us successively, in unlimited sequence, the other so-called "finite cardinal numbers" denoted by 3, 4, 5, . . .   The use which we here make of these numbers as suffixes is justified by the fact that a number is only used as a suffix when it has been defined as a cardinal number. We have, if by $\nu - 1$ is understood the number immediately preceding ν in the above series,

$$(4) \qquad \nu = \overline{\overline{E}}_{\nu-1},$$

$$(5) \qquad E_\nu = (E_{\nu-1},\ e_\nu) = (e_0,\ e_1,\ \ldots e_\nu).$$

From the definition of a sum in § 3 follows :

(6) $$\overline{\overline{E}}_\nu = \overline{\overline{E}}_{\nu-1} + 1 ;$$

that is to say, every cardinal number, except 1, is the sum of the immediately preceding one and 1.

Now, the following three theorems come into the foreground :

A. The terms of the unlimited series of finite cardinal numbers

$$1, 2, 3, \ldots, \nu, \ldots$$

are all different from one another (that is to say, the condition of equivalence established in § 1 is not fulfilled for the corresponding aggregates).

[490] B. Every one of these numbers ν is greater than the preceding ones and less than the following ones (§ 2).

C. There are no cardinal numbers which, in magnitude, lie between two consecutive numbers ν and $\nu + 1$ (§ 2).

We make the proofs of these theorems rest on the two following ones, D and E. We shall, then, in the next place, give the latter theorems rigid proofs.

D. If M is an aggregate such that it is of equal power with none of its parts, then the aggregate (M, e), which arises from M by the addition of a single new element e, has the same property of being of equal power with none of its parts.

E. If N is an aggregate with the finite cardinal number ν, and N_1 is any part of N, the cardinal number of N_1 is equal to one of the preceding numbers 1, 2, 3, . . ., $\nu - 1$.

Proof of D.—Suppose that the aggregate (M, e) is equivalent to one of its parts which we will call N. Then two cases, both of which lead to a contradiction, are to be distinguished :

(*a*) The aggregate N contains e as element ; let $N = (M_1, e)$; then M_1 is a part of M because N is a part of (M, e). As we saw in § 1, the law of correspondence of the two equivalent aggregates (M, e) and (M_1, e) can be so modified that the element e of the one corresponds to the same element e of the other ; by that, then, M and M_1 are referred reciprocally and univocally to one another. But this contradicts the supposition that M is not equivalent to its part M_1.

(*b*) The part N of (M, e) does not contain e as element, so that N is either M or a part of M. In the law of correspondence between (M, e) and N, which lies at the basis of our supposition, to the element e of the former let the element f of the latter correspond. Let $N = (M_1, f)$; then the aggregate M is put in a reciprocally univocal relation with M_1. But M_1 is a part of N and hence of M. So here too M would be equivalent to one of its parts, and this is contrary to the supposition.

Proof of E.—We will suppose the correctness of the theorem up to a certain ν and then conclude its validity for the number $\nu + 1$ which immediately follows, in the following manner :—We start from the aggregate $E_\nu = (e_0, e_1, \ldots, e_\nu)$ as an aggregate with the cardinal number $\nu + 1$. If the theorem is true for this aggregate, its truth for any other aggregate with the same cardinal number $\nu + 1$ follows at once by § 1. Let E′ be any part of E_ν; we distinguish the following cases:

(*a*) E′ does not contain e_ν as element, then E is either $E_{\nu-1}$ **[491]** or a part of $E_{\nu-1}$, and so has as cardinal number either ν or one of the numbers 1, 2, 3, . . ., $\nu - 1$, because we supposed our theorem true for the aggregate $E_{\nu-1}$, with the cardinal number ν.

(*b*) E′ consists of the single element e_ν, then $\overline{\overline{E'}} = 1$.

(*c*) E′ consists of e_ν and an aggregate E″, so that $E' = (E'', e_\nu)$. E″ is a part of $E_{\nu-1}$ and has therefore by supposition as cardinal number one of the numbers 1, 2, 3, . . ., $\nu - 1$. But now $\overline{\overline{E'}} = \overline{\overline{E''}} + 1$, and thus the cardinal number of E′ is one of the numbers 2, 3, . . ., ν.

Proof of A.—Every one of the aggregates which we have denoted by E_ν has the property of not being equivalent to any of its parts. For if we suppose that this is so as far as a certain ν, it follows from the theorem D that it is so for the immediately following number $\nu + 1$. For $\nu = 1$, we recognize at once that the aggregate $E_1 = (e_0, e_1)$ is not equivalent to any of its parts, which are here (e_0) and (e_1). Consider, now, any two numbers μ and ν of the series 1, 2, 3, . . . ; then, if μ is the earlier and ν the later, $E_{\mu-1}$ is a part of $E_{\nu-1}$. Thus $E_{\mu-1}$ and

$E_{\nu-1}$ are not equivalent, and accordingly their cardinal numbers $\mu = \overline{\overline{E}}_{\mu-1}$ and $\nu = \overline{\overline{E}}_{\nu-1}$ are not equal.

Proof of B.—If of the two finite cardinal numbers μ and ν the first is the earlier and the second the later, then $\mu < \nu$. For consider the two aggregates $M = E_{\mu-1}$ and $N = E_{\nu-1}$; for them each of the two conditions in § 2 for $\overline{\overline{M}} < \overline{\overline{N}}$ is fulfilled. The condition (*a*) is fulfilled because, by theorem E, a part of $M = E_{\mu-1}$ can only have one of the cardinal numbers 1, 2, 3, . . ., $\mu - 1$, and therefore, by theorem A, cannot be equivalent to the aggregate $N = E_{\nu-1}$. The condition (*b*) is fulfilled because M itself is a part of N.

Proof of C.—Let $\mathfrak{a}$ be a cardinal number which is less than $\nu + 1$. Because of the condition (*b*) of § 2, there is a part of E_ν with the cardinal number $\mathfrak{a}$. By theorem E, a part of E_ν can only have one of the cardinal numbers 1, 2, 3, . . ., ν. Thus $\mathfrak{a}$ is equal to one of the cardinal numbers 1, 2, 3, . . ., ν. By theorem B, none of these is greater than ν. Consequently there is no cardinal number $\mathfrak{a}$ which is less than $\nu + 1$ and greater than ν.

Of importance for what follows is the following theorem :

F. If K is any aggregate of different finite cardinal numbers, there is one, κ_1, amongst them which is smaller than the rest, and therefore the smallest of all.

[492] *Proof.*—The aggregate K either contains

the number 1, in which case it is the least, $\kappa_1 = 1$, or it does not. In the latter case, let J be the aggregate of all those cardinal numbers of our series, 1, 2, 3, . . ., which are smaller than those occurring in K. If a number ν belongs to J, all numbers less than ν belong to J. But J must have one element ν_1 such that $\nu_1 + 1$, and consequently all greater numbers, do not belong to J, because otherwise J would contain all finite numbers, whereas the numbers belonging to K are not contained in J. Thus J is the segment (*Abschnitt*) (1, 2, 3, . . ., ν_1). The number $\nu_1 + 1 = \kappa_1$ is necessarily an element of K and smaller than the rest.

From F we conclude :

G. Every aggregate $K = \{\kappa\}$ of different finite cardinal numbers can be brought into the form of a series

$$K = (\kappa_1, \kappa_2, \kappa_3, \ldots)$$

such that

$$\kappa_1 < \kappa_2 < \kappa_3, \ldots$$

§ 6

The Smallest Transfinite Cardinal Number Aleph-Zero

Aggregates with finite cardinal numbers are called "finite aggregates," all others we will call "transfinite aggregates" and their cardinal numbers "transfinite cardinal numbers."

The first example of a transfinite aggregate is given by the totality of finite cardinal numbers ν ;

we call its cardinal number (§ 1) " Aleph-zero " and denote it by $\aleph_0$; thus we define

$$(1) \qquad\qquad \aleph_0 = \overline{\overline{\{\nu\}}}.$$

That $\aleph_0$ is a *transfinite* number, that is to say, is not equal to any finite number μ, follows from the simple fact that, if to the aggregate $\{\nu\}$ is added a new element e_0, the union-aggregate $(\{\nu\}, e_0)$ is equivalent to the original aggregate $\{\nu\}$. For we can think of this reciprocally univocal correspondence between them : to the element e_0 of the first corresponds the element 1 of the second, and to the element ν of the first corresponds the element $\nu + 1$ of the other. By § 3 we thus have

$$(2) \qquad\qquad \aleph_0 + 1 = \aleph_0.$$

But we showed in § 5 that $\mu + 1$ is always different from μ, and therefore $\aleph_0$ is not equal to any finite number μ.

The number $\aleph_0$ is greater than any finite number μ :

$$(3) \qquad\qquad \aleph_0 > \mu.$$

[493] This follows, if we pay attention to § 3, from the three facts that $\mu = (1, \overline{2, 3, \ldots, \mu})$, that no part of the aggregate $(1, 2, 3, \ldots, \mu)$ is equivalent to the aggregate $\{\nu\}$, and that $(1, 2, 3, \ldots, \mu)$ is itself a part of $\{\nu\}$.

On the other hand, $\aleph_0$ is the least transfinite cardinal number. If $\mathfrak{a}$ is any transfinite cardinal number different from $\aleph_0$, then

$$(4) \qquad\qquad \aleph_0 < \mathfrak{a}.$$

This rests on the following theorems :

A. Every transfinite aggregate T has parts with the cardinal number $\aleph_0$.

Proof.—If, by any rule, we have taken away a finite number of elements t_1, t_2, . . ., $t_{\nu-1}$, there always remains the possibility of taking away a further element t_ν. The aggregate $\{t_\nu\}$, where ν denotes any finite cardinal number, is a part of T with the cardinal number $\aleph_0$, because $\{t_\nu\} \backsim \{\nu\}$ (§ 1).

B. If S is a transfinite aggregate with the cardinal number $\aleph_0$, and S_1 is any transfinite part of S, then $\overline{\overline{S}}_1 = \aleph_0$.

Proof.—We have supposed that $S \backsim \{\nu\}$. Choose a definite law of correspondence between these two aggregates, and, with this law, denote by s_ν that element of S which corresponds to the element ν of $\{\nu\}$, so that

$$S = \{s_\nu\}.$$

The part S_1 of S consists of certain elements s_κ of S, and the totality of numbers κ forms a transfinite part K of the aggregate $\{\nu\}$. By theorem G of § 5 the aggregate K can be brought into the form of a series

$$K = \{\kappa_\nu\},$$

where

$$\kappa_\nu < \kappa_{\nu+1} ;$$

consequently we have

$$S_1 = \{s_{\kappa_\nu}\}.$$

Hence follows that $S_1 \backsim S$, and therefore $\overline{\overline{S_1}} = \aleph_0$.

From A and B the formula (4) results, if we have regard to § 2.

From (2) we conclude, by adding 1 to both sides,

$$\aleph_0 + 2 = \aleph_0 + 1 = \aleph_0,$$

and, by repeating this

(5) $$\aleph_0 + \nu = \aleph_0.$$

We have also

(6) $$\aleph_0 + \aleph_0 = \aleph_0.$$

[494] For, by (1) of § 3, $\aleph_0 + \aleph_0$ is the cardinal number $\overline{\overline{(\{a_\nu\}, \{b_\nu\})}}$ because

$$\overline{\overline{\{a_\nu\}}} = \overline{\overline{\{b_\nu\}}} = \aleph_0.$$

Now, obviously

$$\{\nu\} = (\{2\nu - 1\}, \{2\nu\}),$$
$$(\{2\nu - 1\}, \{2\nu\}) \backsim (\{a_\nu\}, \{b_\nu\}),$$

and therefore

$$\overline{\overline{(\{a_\nu\}, \{b_\nu\})}} = \overline{\overline{\{\nu\}}} = \aleph_0.$$

The equation (6) can also be written

$$\aleph_0 \cdot 2 = \aleph_0 ;$$

and, by adding $\aleph_0$ repeatedly to both sides, we find that

(7) $$\aleph_0 \cdot \nu = \nu \cdot \aleph_0 = \aleph_0.$$

We also have

(8) $$\aleph_0 \cdot \aleph_0 = \aleph_0.$$

Proof.—By (6) of § 3, $\aleph_0 \cdot \aleph_0$ is the cardinal number of the aggregate of bindings

$$\{(\mu, \nu)\},$$

where μ and ν are any finite cardinal numbers which are independent of one another. If also λ represents any finite cardinal number, so that $\{\lambda\}$, $\{\mu\}$, and $\{\nu\}$ are only different notations for the same aggregate of all finite numbers, we have to show that

$$\{(\mu, \nu)\} \backsim \{\lambda\}.$$

Let us denote $\mu + \nu$ by ρ; then ρ takes all the numerical values 2, 3, 4, . . ., and there are in all $\rho - 1$ elements (μ, ν) for which $\mu + \nu = \rho$, namely :

$$(1, \rho - 1), (2, \rho - 2), \ldots, (\rho - 1, 1).$$

In this sequence imagine first the element $(1, 1)$, for which $\rho = 2$, put, then the two elements for which $\rho = 3$, then the three elements for which $\rho = 4$, and so on. Thus we get all the elements (μ, ν) in a simple series :

$$(1, 1); (1, 2), (2, 1); (1, 3), (2, 2), (3, 1); (1, 4), (2, 3), \ldots,$$

and here, as we easily see, the element (μ, ν) comes at the λth place, where

$$(9) \qquad \lambda = \mu + \frac{(\mu + \nu - 1)(\mu + \nu - 2)}{2}.$$

The variable λ takes every numerical value 1, 2, 3, . . ., once. Consequently, by means of (9), a reciprocally univocal relation subsists between the aggregates $\{\nu\}$ and $\{(\mu, \nu)\}$.

[495] If both sides of the equation (8) are multiplied by $\aleph_0$, we get $\aleph_0^3 = \aleph_0^2 = \aleph_0$, and, by repeated multiplications by $\aleph_0$, we get the equation, valid for every finite cardinal number ν :

$$(10) \qquad\qquad \aleph_0^\nu = \aleph_0.$$

The theorems E and A of § 5 lead to this theorem on finite aggregates :

C. Every finite aggregate E is such that it is equivalent to none of its parts.

This theorem stands sharply opposed to the following one for transfinite aggregates :

D. Every transfinite aggregate T is such that it has parts T_1 which are equivalent to it.

Proof.—By theorem A of this paragraph there is a part $S = \{t_\nu\}$ of T with the cardinal number $\aleph_0$. Let $T = (S, U)$, so that U is composed of those elements of T which are different from the elements t_ν. Let us put $S_1 = \{t_{\nu+1}\}$, $T_1 = (S_1, U)$; then T_1 is a part of T, and, in fact, that part which arises out of T if we leave out the single element t_1. Since $S \backsim S_1$, by theorem B of this paragraph, and $U \backsim U$, we have, by § 1, $T \backsim T_1$.

In these theorems C and D the essential difference between finite and transfinite aggregates, to which I referred in the year 1877, in volume lxxxiv [1878] of Crelle's *Journal*, p. 242, appears in the clearest way.

After we have introduced the least transfinite

cardinal number $\aleph_0$ and derived its properties that lie the most readily to hand, the question arises as to the higher cardinal numbers and how they proceed from $\aleph_0$. We shall show that the transfinite cardinal numbers can be arranged according to their magnitude, and, in this order, form, like the finite numbers, a "well-ordered aggregate" in an extended sense of the words. Out of $\aleph_0$ proceeds, by a definite law, the next greater cardinal number $\aleph_1$, out of this by the same law the next greater $\aleph_2$, and so on. But even the unlimited sequence of cardinal numbers

$$\aleph_0, \aleph_1, \aleph_2, \ldots, \aleph_\nu, \ldots$$

does not exhaust the conception of transfinite cardinal number. We will prove the existence of a cardinal number which we denote by $\aleph_\omega$ and which shows itself to be the next greater to all the numbers $\aleph_\nu$; out of it proceeds in the same way as $\aleph_1$ out of $\aleph$ a next greater $\aleph_{\omega+1}$, and so on, without end.

[496] To every transfinite cardinal number a there is a next greater proceeding out of it according to a unitary law, and also to every unlimitedly ascending well-ordered aggregate of transfinite cardinal numbers, $\{a\}$, there is a next greater proceeding out of that aggregate in a unitary way.

For the rigorous foundation of this matter, discovered in 1882 and exposed in the pamphlet *Grundlagen einer allgemeinen Mannichfaltigkeitslehre* (Leipzig, 1883) and in volume xxi of the

Mathematische Annalen, we make use of the so-called "ordinal types" whose theory we have to set forth in the following paragraphs.

§ 7

The Ordinal Types of Simply Ordered Aggregates

We call an aggregate M "simply ordered" if a definite "order of precedence" (*Rangordnung*) rules over its elements m, so that, of every two elements m_1 and m_2, one takes the "lower" and the other the "higher" rank, and so that, if of three elements m_1, m_2, and m_3, m_1, say, is of lower rank than m_2, and m_2 is of lower rank than m_3, then m_1 is of lower rank than m_3.

The relation of two elements m_1 and m_2, in which m_1 has the lower rank in the given order of precedence and m_2 the higher, is expressed by the formulæ :

(1) $$m_1 < m_2, \quad m_2 > m_1.$$

Thus, for example, every aggregate P of points defined on a straight line is a simply ordered aggregate if, of every two points p_1 and p_2 belonging to it, that one whose co-ordinate (an origin and a positive direction having been fixed upon) is the lesser is given the lower rank.

It is evident that one and the same aggregate can be "simply ordered" according to the most different laws. Thus, for example, with the aggregate R of all positive rational numbers p/q (where p and q are relatively prime integers) which are greater than o and less than 1, there is, firstly, their "natural" order according to magnitude ; then they can be arranged (and in this order we will denote the aggregate by R_0) so that, of two numbers p_1/q_1 and p_2/q_2 for which the sums p_1+q_1 and p_2+q_2 have different values, that number for which the corresponding sum is less takes the lower rank, and, if $p_1+q_1=p_2+q_2$, then the smaller of the two rational numbers is the lower. **[497]** In this order of precedence, our aggregate, since to one and the same value of $p+q$ only a finite number of rational numbers p/q belongs, evidently has the form

$$R_0=(r_1, r_2, \ldots, r_\nu, \ldots)=(\tfrac{1}{2}, \tfrac{1}{3}, \tfrac{1}{4}, \tfrac{2}{3}, \tfrac{1}{5}, \tfrac{1}{6}, \tfrac{2}{5}, \tfrac{3}{4}, \ldots),$$

where

$$r_\nu \prec r_{\nu+1}.$$

Always, then, when we speak of a "simply ordered" aggregate M, we imagine laid down a definite order or precedence of its elements, in the sense explained above.

There are doubly, triply, ν-ply and $\mathfrak{a}$-ply ordered aggregates, but for the present we will not consider them. So in what follows we will use the shorter expression "ordered aggregate" when we mean "simply ordered aggregate."

Every ordered aggregate M has a definite "ordinal type," or more shortly a definite "type," which we will denote by

(2) $\overline{M}$.

By this we understand the general concept which results from M if we only abstract from the nature of the elements m, and retain the order of precedence among them. Thus the ordinal type $\overline{M}$ is itself an ordered aggregate whose elements are units which have the same order of precedence amongst one another as the corresponding elements of M, from which they are derived by abstraction.

We call two ordered aggregates M and N "similar" (*ähnlich*) if they can be put into a bi-univocal correspondence with one another in such a manner that, if m_1 and m_2 are any two elements of M and n_1 and n_2 the corresponding elements of N, then the relation of rank of m_1 to m_2 in M is the same as that of n_1 to n_2 in N. Such a correspondence of similar aggregates we call an "imaging" (*Abbildung*) of these aggregates on one another. In such an imaging, to every part—which obviously also appears as an ordered aggregate—M_1 of M corresponds a similar part N_1 of N.

We express the similarity of two ordered aggregates M and N by the formula :

(3) $$M \sim N.$$

Every ordered aggregate is similar to itself.

If two ordered aggregates are similar to a third, they are similar to one another.

[498] A simple consideration shows that two ordered aggregates have the same ordinal type if, and only if, they are similar, so that, of the two formulæ

$$(4) \qquad \overline{M} = \overline{N}, \quad M \backsim N,$$

one is always a consequence of the other.

If, with an ordinal type $\overline{M}$ we also abstract from the order of precedence of the elements, we get (§ 1) the cardinal number $\overline{\overline{M}}$ of the ordered aggregate M, which is, at the same time, the cardinal number of the ordinal type $\overline{M}$. From $\overline{M} = \overline{N}$ always follows $\overline{\overline{M}} = \overline{\overline{N}}$, that is to say, ordered aggregates of equal types always have the same power or cardinal number ; from the similarity of ordered aggregates follows their equivalence. On the other hand, two aggregates may be equivalent without being similar.

We will use the small letters of the Greek alphabet to denote ordinal types. If a is an ordinal type, we understand by

$$(5) \qquad \bar{a}$$

its corresponding cardinal number.

The ordinal types of finite ordered aggregates offer no special interest. For we easily convince ourselves that, for one and the same finite cardinal number ν, all simply ordered aggregates are similar to one another, and thus have one and the same type. Thus the finite simple ordinal types are subject to the same laws as the finite cardinal numbers, and it is allowable to use the same signs 1, 2, 3, . . ., ν, . . . for them, although they are conceptually different from the cardinal numbers. The case is quite different with the transfinite ordinal types ; for to one and the same cardinal number belong innumerably many different types of simply ordered aggregates, which, in their totality, constitute a particular "class of types" (*Typenclasse*). Every one of these classes of types is, therefore, determined by the transfinite cardinal number $\mathfrak{a}$ which is common to all the types belonging to the class. Thus we call it for short the class of types $[\mathfrak{a}]$. That class which naturally presents itself first to us, and whose complete investigation must, accordingly, be the next special aim of the theory of transfinite aggregates, is the class of types $[\aleph_0]$ which embraces all the types with the least transfinite cardinal number $\aleph_0$. From the cardinal number which *determines* the class of types $[\mathfrak{a}]$ we have to distinguish that cardinal number $\mathfrak{a}'$ which for its part **[499]** *is determined by* the class of types $[\mathfrak{a}]$. The latter is the cardinal number which (§ 1) the class $[\mathfrak{a}]$ has, in so far as it represents a well-defined aggregate whose elements are all the types α with the cardinal number $\mathfrak{a}$. We will see that $\mathfrak{a}'$ is different from $\mathfrak{a}$, and indeed always greater than $\mathfrak{a}$.

If in an ordered aggregate M all the relations of precedence of its elements are inverted, so that "lower" becomes "higher" and "higher" becomes "lower" everywhere, we again get an ordered aggregate, which we will denote by

$$(6) \qquad\qquad *M$$

and call the "inverse" of M. We denote the ordinal type of *M, if $\alpha = \overline{M}$, by

$$(7) \qquad\qquad *\alpha.$$

It may happen that $^*a = a$, as, for example, in the case of finite types or in that of the type of the aggregate of all rational numbers which are greater than o and less than 1 in their natural order of precedence. This type we will investigate under the notation η.

We remark further that two similarly ordered aggregates can be imaged on one another either in one manner or in many manners; in the first case the type in question is similar to itself in only one way, in the second case in many ways. Not only all finite types, but the types of transfinite "well-ordered aggregates," which will occupy us later and which we call transfinite "ordinal numbers," are such that they allow only a single imaging on themselves. On the other hand, the type η is similar to itself in an infinity of ways.

We will make this difference clear by two simple examples. By ω we understand the type of a well-ordered aggregate

$$(e_1, \ e_2, \ \ldots, \ e_\nu, \ \ldots),$$

in which

$$e_\nu < e_{\nu+1},$$

and where ν represents all finite cardinal numbers in turn. Another well-ordered aggregate

$$(f_1, \ f_2, \ \ldots, \ f_\nu, \ \ldots),$$

with the condition

$$f_\nu < f_{\nu+1},$$

of the same type ω can obviously only be imaged

on the former in such a way that e_ν and f_ν are corresponding elements. For e_1, the lowest element in rank of the first, must, in the process of imaging, be correlated to the lowest element f_1 of the second, the next after e_1 in rank (e_2) to f_2, the next after f_1, and so on. [500] Every other bi-univocal correspondence of the two equivalent aggregates $\{e_\nu\}$ and $\{f_\nu\}$ is not an "imaging" in the sense which we have fixed above for the theory of types.

On the other hand, let us take an ordered aggregate of the form

$$\{e_\nu\},$$

where ν represents all positive and negative finite integers, including 0, and where likewise

$$e_\nu \prec e_{\nu+1}.$$

This aggregate has no lowest and no highest element in rank. Its type is, by the definition of a sum given in § 8,

$$*\omega+\omega.$$

It is similar to itself in an infinity of ways. For let us consider an aggregate of the same type

$$\{f_{\nu'}\},$$

where

$$f_{\nu'} \prec f_{\nu'+1}.$$

Then the two ordered aggregates can be so imaged on one another that, if we understand by ν_0' a definite one of the numbers ν', to the element e_ν of the first the element $f_{\nu_0'+\nu'}$ of the second corresponds. Since ν_0' is arbitrary, we have here an infinity of imagings.

The concept of "ordinal type" developed here, when it is transferred in like manner to "multiply ordered aggregates," embraces, in conjunction with the concept of "cardinal number" or "power" introduced in § 1, everything capable of being numbered (*Anzahlmässige*) that is thinkable, and in this sense cannot be further generalized. It contains nothing arbitrary, but is the natural extension of the concept of number. It deserves to be especially emphasized that the criterion of equality (4) follows with absolute necessity from the concept of ordinal type and consequently permits of no alteration. The chief cause of the grave errors in G. Veronese's *Grundzüge der Geometrie* (German by A. Schepp, Leipzig, 1894) is the non-recognition of this point.

On page 30 the "number (*Anzahl oder Zahl*) of an ordered group" is defined in exactly the same way as what we have called the "ordinal type of a simply ordered aggregate" (*Zur Lehre vom Transfiniten*, Halle, 1890, pp. 68–75 ; reprinted from the *Zeitschr. für Philos. und philos. Kritik* for 1887). **[501]** But Veronese thinks that he must make an addition to the criterion of equality. He says on page 31 : "Numbers whose units correspond to one another uniquely and in the same order and of which the one is neither a part of the other nor equal to a part of the other are

equal."* This definition of equality contains a
circle and thus is meaningless. For what is
the meaning of "not equal to a part of the
other" in this addition? To answer this question,
we must first know when two numbers are equal
or unequal. Thus, apart from the arbitrariness
of his definition of equality, it presupposes a
definition of equality, and this again presupposes
a definition of equality, in which we must know
again what equal and unequal are, and so on *ad
infinitum*. After Veronese has, so to speak, given
up of his own free will the indispensable foundation
for the comparison of numbers, we ought not to
be surprised at the lawlessness with which, later
on, he operates with his pseudo-transfinite numbers,
and ascribes properties to them which they cannot
possess simply because they themselves, in the
form imagined by him, have no existence except
on paper. Thus, too, the striking similarity of his
"numbers" to the very absurd "infinite numbers"
in Fontenelle's *Géométrie de l'Infini* (Paris, 1727)
becomes comprehensible. Recently, W. Killing
has given welcome expression to his doubts concerning the foundation of Veronese's book in the
Index lectionum of the Münster Academy for 1895–
1896.†

* In the original Italian edition (p. 27) this passage runs: "Numeri
le unità dei quali si corrispondono univocamente e nel medesimo ordine,
e di cui l' uno non è parte o uguale ad una parte dell' altro, sono uguali."
† [Veronese replied to this in *Math. Ann.*, vol. xlvii, 1897, pp. 423–
432. *Cf.* Killing, *ibid.*, vol. xlviii, 1897, pp. 425–432.]

§ 8

Addition and Multiplication of Ordinal Types

The union-aggregate (M, N) of two aggregates M and N can, if M and N are ordered, be conceived as an ordered aggregate in which the relations of precedence of the elements of M among themselves as well as the relations of precedence of the elements of N among themselves remain the same as in M or N respectively, and all elements of M have a lower rank than all the elements of N. If M′ and N′ are two other ordered aggregates, M $\backsim$ M′ and N $\underset{\sim}{}$ N′, [502] then (M, N) $\backsim$ (M′, N′); so the ordinal type of (M, N) depends only on the ordinal types $\overline{M} = \alpha$ and $\overline{N} = \beta$. Thus, we define:

$$(1) \qquad \alpha + \beta = (\overline{M, N}).$$

In the sum $\alpha + \beta$ we call α the "augend" and β the "addend."

For any three types we easily prove the associative law :

$$(2) \qquad \alpha + (\beta + \gamma) = (\alpha + \beta) + \gamma.$$

On the other hand, the commutative law is not valid, in general, for the addition of types. We see this by the following simple example.

If ω is the type, already mentioned in § 7, of the well-ordered aggregate

$$E = (e_1, e_2, \ldots e_\nu \ldots), \quad e_\nu < e_{\nu+1},$$

then $1 + \omega$ is not equal to $\omega + 1$. For, if f is a new element, we have by (1) :

$$1 + \omega = \overline{(f, \mathrm{E})},$$
$$\omega + 1 = \overline{(\mathrm{E}, f)}.$$

But the aggregate

$$(f, \mathrm{E}) = (f, e_1, e_2, \ldots, e_\nu, \ldots)$$

is similar to the aggregate E, and consequently

$$1 + \omega = \omega.$$

On the contrary, the aggregates E and (E, f) are not similar, because the first has no term which is highest in rank, but the second has the highest term f. Thus $\omega + 1$ is different from $\omega = 1 + \omega$.

Out of two ordered aggregates M and N with the types α and β we can set up an ordered aggregate S by substituting for every element n of N an ordered aggregate M_n which has the same type α as M, so that

$$(3) \qquad\qquad \overline{\mathrm{M}}_n = \alpha;$$

and, for the order of precedence in

$$(4) \qquad\qquad \mathrm{S} = \{\mathrm{M}_n\}$$

we make the two rules :

(1) Every two elements of S which belong to one and the same aggregate M_n are to retain in S the same order of precedence as in M_n ;

(2) Every two elements of S which belong to two different aggregates M_{n_1} and M_{n_2} have the same relation of precedence as n_1 and n_2 have in N.

The ordinal type of S depends, as we easily see, only on the types a and β; we define

(5) $\qquad\qquad a \cdot \beta = \overline{S}.$

[503] In this product a is called the "multiplicand" and β the "multiplier."

In any definite imaging of M on M_n let m_n be the element of M_n that corresponds to the element m of M; we can then also write

(6) $\qquad\qquad S = \{m_n\}.$

Consider a third ordered aggregate $P = \{p\}$ with the ordinal type $\overline{P} = \gamma$, then, by (5),

$$a \cdot \beta = \overline{\{m_n\}}, \quad \beta \cdot \gamma = \overline{\{n_p\}}, \quad (a \cdot \beta) \cdot \gamma = \overline{\{(m_n)_p\}},$$
$$a \cdot (\beta \cdot \gamma) = \overline{\{m_{(n_p)}\}}.$$

But the two ordered aggregates $\{(m_n)_p\}$ and $\{m_{(n_p)}\}$ are similar, and are imaged on one another if we regard the elements $(m_n)_p$ and $m_{(n_p)}$ as corresponding. Consequently, for three types a, β, and γ the associative law

(7) $\qquad\qquad (a \cdot \beta) \cdot \gamma = a \cdot (\beta \cdot \gamma)$

subsists. From (1) and (5) follows easily the distributive law

(8) $\qquad\qquad a \cdot (\beta + \gamma) = a \cdot \beta + a \cdot \gamma;$

but only in this form, where the factor with two terms is the multiplier.

On the contrary, in the multiplication of types as in their addition, the commutative law is not generally valid. For example, $2 . \omega$ and $\omega . 2$ are different types; for, by (5),

$$2 . \omega = \overline{(e_1, f_1; \ e_2, f_2; \ \ldots; \ e_\nu, f_\nu; \ \ldots)} = \omega;$$

while

$$\omega . 2 = \overline{(e_1, e_2, \ldots, e_\nu, \ldots; \ f_1, f_2, \ldots, f_\nu, \ldots)}$$

is obviously different from ω.

If we compare the definitions of the elementary operations for cardinal numbers, given in § 3, with those established here for ordinal types, we easily see that the cardinal number of the sum of two types is equal to the sum of the cardinal numbers of the single types, and that the cardinal number of the product of two types is equal to the product of the cardinal numbers of the single types. Every equation between ordinal types which proceeds from the two elementary operations remains correct, therefore, if we replace in it all the types by their cardinal numbers.

[504]   § 9

The Ordinal Type η of the Aggregate R of all Rational Numbers which are Greater than 0 and Smaller than 1, in their Natural Order of Precedence

By R we understand, as in § 7, the system of all rational numbers p/q (p and q being relatively prime) which > 0 and < 1, in their natural order of precedence, where the magnitude of a number determines its rank. We denote the ordinal type of R by η:

(1) $$\eta = \overline{R}.$$

But we have put the same aggregate in another order of precedence in which we call it R_0. This order is determined, in the first place, by the magnitude of $p + q$, and in the second place—for rational numbers for which $p + q$ has the same value —by the magnitude of p/q itself. The aggregate R_0 is a well-ordered aggregate of type ω:

(2) $R_0 = (r_1, r_2, \ldots, r_\nu, \ldots)$, where $r_\nu < r_{\nu+1}$,

(3) $\overline{R}_0 = \omega$.

Both R and R_0 have the same cardinal number since they only differ in the order of precedence of their elements, and, since we obviously have $\overline{\overline{R}}_0 = \aleph_0$, we also have

(4) $$\overline{\overline{R}} = \overline{\eta} = \aleph_0.$$

Thus the type η belongs to the class of types $[\aleph_0]$.

Secondly, we remark that in R there is neither an element which is lowest in rank nor one which is highest in rank. Thirdly, R has the property that between every two of its elements others lie. This property we express by the words: R is "everywhere dense" (*überalldicht*).

We will now show that these three properties characterize the type η of R, so that we have the following theorem:

If we have a simply ordered aggregate M such that

(*a*) $\overline{\overline{M}} = \aleph_0$;

(*b*) M has no element which is lowest in rank, and no highest ;

(*c*) M is everywhere dense ;

then the ordinal type of M is η :

$$\overline{M} = \eta.$$

Proof.—Because of the condition (*a*), M can be brought into the form **[505]** of a well-ordered aggregate of type ω ; having fixed upon such a form, we denote it by M_0 and put

(5) $M_0 = (m_1, \ m_2, \ \ldots, \ m_\nu, \ \ldots).$

We have now to show that

(6) $M \smallsmile R$;

that is to say, we must prove that M can be imaged on R in such a way that the relation of precedence of any and every two elements in M is the same as that of the two corresponding elements in R.

Let the element r_1 in R be correlated to the element m_1 in M. The element r_2 has a definite relation of precedence to r_1 in R. Because of the condition (*b*), there are infinitely many elements m_ν of M which have the same relation of precedence in M to m_1 as r_2 to r_1 in R ; of them we choose that one which has the smallest index in M_0, let it be m_{ι_2} and correlate it to r_2. The element r_3 has in R definite relations of precedence to r_1 and r_2 ; because of the conditions (*b*) and (*c*) there is an infinity of elements m_ν of M which have the same relation of precedence to m_1 and m_{ι_2} in M as r_3 to r_1 and r_2 to R ; of them we choose that—let it be m_{ι_2} —which has the smallest index in M_0, and correlate it to r_3. According to this law we imagine the process of correlation continued.   If to the ν elements

$$r_1, \; r_2, \; r_3, \; \ldots, \; r_\nu$$

of R are correlated, as images, definite elements

$$m_1, \; m_{\iota_2}, \; m_{\iota_3}, \; \ldots, \; m_{\iota_\nu},$$

which have the same relations of precedence amongst one another in M as the corresponding elements in R, then to the element $r_{\nu+1}$ of R is to be correlated that element $m_{\iota_{\nu+1}}$ of M which has the smallest index in M_0 of those which have the same relations of precedence to

$$m_1, \; m_{\iota_2}, \; m_{\iota_3}, \; \ldots, \; m_{\iota_\nu}$$

in M as $r_{\nu+1}$ to $r_1, \; r_2, \; \ldots, \; r_\nu$ in R.

In this manner we have correlated definite elements m_{ι_ν} of M to all the elements r_ν of R, and the elements m_{ι_ν} have in M the same order of precedence as the corresponding elements r_ν in R.   But we have still to show that the elements m_{ι_ν} include *all* the elements m_ν of M, or, what is the same thing, that the series

$$1, \; \iota_2, \; \iota_3, \; \ldots, \; \iota_\nu, \; \ldots$$

[506] is only a permutation of the series

$$1, \; 2, \; 3, \; \ldots \; \nu, \; \ldots$$

We prove this by a complete induction: we will show that, if the elements m_1, m_2, ..., m_ν appear in the imaging, that is also the case with the following element $m_{\nu+1}$.

Let λ be so great that, among the elements

$$m_1, m_{\iota_2}, m_{\iota_3}, \ldots, m_{\iota_\lambda},$$

the elements

$$m_1, m_2, \ldots, m_\nu,$$

which, by supposition, appear in the imaging, are contained. It may be that also $m_{\nu+1}$ is found among them; then $m_{\nu+1}$ appears in the imaging. But if $m_{\nu+1}$ is not among the elements

$$m_1, m_{\iota_2}, m_{\iota_3}, \ldots, m_{\iota_\lambda},$$

then $m_{\nu+1}$ has with respect to these elements a definite ordinal position in M; infinitely many elements in R have the same ordinal position in R with respect to r_1, r_2, ..., r_λ, amongst which let $r_{\lambda+\sigma}$ be that with the least index in R_0. Then $m_{\nu+1}$ has, as we can easily make sure, the same ordinal position with respect to

$$m_1, m_{\iota_2}, m_{\iota_3}, \ldots, m_{\iota_{\lambda+\sigma-1}}$$

in M as $r_{\lambda+\sigma}$ has with respect to

$$r_1, r_2, \ldots, r_{\lambda+\sigma-1}$$

in R. Since m_1, m_2, ..., m_ν have already appeared in the imaging, $m_{\nu+1}$ is that element with the smallest index in M which has this ordinal position with respect to

$$m_1, m_{\iota_2}, \ldots, m_{\iota_{\lambda+\sigma-1}}.$$

Consequently, according to our law of correlation,

$$m_{\iota_{\lambda+\sigma}} = m_{\nu+1}.$$

Thus, in this case too, the element $m_{\nu+1}$ appears in the imaging, and $r_{\lambda+\sigma}$ is the element of R which is correlated to it.

We see, then, that by our manner of correlation, the *whole aggregate* M is imaged on the *whole aggregate* R; M and R are similar aggregates, which was to be proved.

From the theorem which we have just proved result, for example, the following theorems :

[507] The ordinal type of the aggregate of all negative and positive rational numbers, including zero, in their natural order of precedence, is η.

The ordinal type of the aggregate of all rational numbers which are greater than a and less than b, in their natural order of precedence, where a and b are any real numbers, and $a < b$, is η.

The ordinal type of the aggregate of all real algebraic numbers in their natural order of precedence is η.

The ordinal type of the aggregate of all real algebraic numbers which are greater than a and less than b, in their natural order of precedence, where a and b are any real numbers and $a < b$, is η.

For all these ordered aggregates satisfy the three conditions required in our theorem for M (see Crelle's *Journal*, vol. lxxvii. p. 258).*

If we consider, further, aggregates with the types —according to the definitions given in § 8—written

[* *Cf.* Section V of the Introduction.]

$\eta + \eta$, $\eta\eta$, $(1 + \eta)\eta$, $(\eta + 1)\eta$, $(1 + \eta + 1)\eta$, we find that those three conditions are also fulfilled with them. Thus we have the theorems:

$$(7) \qquad \eta + \eta = \eta,$$
$$(8) \qquad \eta\eta = \eta,$$
$$(9) \qquad (1 + \eta)\eta = \eta,$$
$$(10) \qquad (\eta + 1)\eta = \eta,$$
$$(11) \qquad (1 + \eta + 1)\eta = \eta.$$

The repeated application of (7) and (8) gives for every finite number ν:

$$(12) \qquad \eta \cdot \nu = \eta,$$
$$(13) \qquad \eta^\nu = \eta.$$

On the other hand we easily see that, for $\nu > 1$, the types $1 + \eta$, $\eta + 1$, $\nu . \eta$, $1 + \eta + 1$ are different both from one another and from η. We have

$$(14) \qquad \eta + 1 + \eta = \eta,$$

but $\eta + \nu + \eta$, for $\nu > 1$, is different from η.

Finally, it deserves to be emphasized that

$$(15) \qquad {}^*\eta = \eta.$$

[508] § 10

The Fundamental Series contained in a Transfinite Ordered Aggregate

Let us consider any simply ordered transfinite aggregate M. Every part of M is itself an ordered aggregate. For the study of the type $\overline{M}$, those parts of M which have the types ω and $*\omega$ appear to be especially valuable ; we call them " fundamental series of the first order contained in M," and the former—of type ω—we call an " ascending " series, the latter—of type $*\omega$—a " descending " one.   Since we limit ourselves to the consideration of fundamental series of the first order (in later investigations fundamental series of higher order will also occupy us), we will here simply call them " fundamental series."   Thus an " ascending fundamental series " is of the form

(1) $\{a_\nu\}$,   where $a_\nu < a_{\nu+1}$;

a " descending fundamental series " is of the form

(2) $\{b_\nu\}$,   where $b_\nu > b_{\nu+1}$.

The letter ν, as well as κ, λ, and μ, has everywhere in our considerations the signification of an arbitrary finite cardinal number or of a finite type (a finite ordinal number).

We call two ascending fundamental series $\{a_\nu\}$ and $\{a'_\nu\}$ in M "coherent" (*zusammengehörig*), in signs

(3) $\{a_\nu\} \parallel \{a'_\nu\}$,

if, for every element a_ν there are elements a'_λ such that

$$a_\nu < a'_\lambda,$$

and also for every element a'_ν there are elements a_μ such that

$$a'_\nu < a_\mu.$$

Two descending fundamental series $\{b_\nu\}$ and $\{b'_\nu\}$ in M are said to be "coherent," in signs

(4) $$\{b_\nu\} \parallel \{b'_\nu\},$$

if for every element b_ν there are elements b'_λ such that

$$b_\nu > b'_\lambda,$$

and for every element b'_ν there are elements b_μ such that

$$b'_\nu > b_\mu.$$

An ascending fundamental series $\{a_\nu\}$ and a descending one $\{b_\nu\}$ are said to be "coherent," in signs

[509] (5) $$\{a_\nu\} \parallel \{b_\nu\},$$

if (*a*) for all values of ν and μ

$$a_\nu < b_\mu,$$

and (*b*) in M exists at most one (thus either only one or none at all) element m_0 such that, for all ν's,

$$a_\nu < m_0 < b_\nu.$$

Then we have the theorems :

A. If two fundamental series are coherent to a third, they are also coherent to one another.

B. Two fundamental series proceeding in the same direction of which one is part of the other are coherent.

If there exists in M an element m_0 which has

such a position with respect to the ascending fundamental series $\{a_\nu\}$ that :

(*a*) for every ν

$$a_\nu \lessdot m_0,$$

(*b*) for every element m of M that precedes m_0 there exists a certain number ν_0 such that

$$a_\nu \gtrdot m, \quad \text{for} \quad \nu \gtreqqless \nu_0,$$

then we will call m_0 a "limiting element (*Grenzelement*) of $\{a_\nu\}$ in M" and also a "principal element (*Hauptelement*) of M." In the same way we call m_0 a "principal element of M" and also "limiting element of $\{b_\nu\}$ in M" if these conditions are satisfied :

(*a*) for every ν

$$b_\nu \gtrdot m_0,$$

(*b*) for every element m of M that follows m_0 exists a certain number ν_0 such that

$$b_\nu \gtrdot m, \quad \text{for} \quad \nu \gtreqqless \nu_0.$$

A fundamental series can never have more than one limiting element in M ; but M has, in general, many principal elements.

We perceive the truth of the following theorems :

C. If a fundamental series has a limiting element in M, all fundamental series coherent to it have the same limiting element in M.

D. If two fundamental series (whether proceeding in the same or in opposite directions) have one and the same limiting element in M, they are coherent.

If M and M′ are two similarly ordered aggregates, so that

(6) $\overline{M} = \overline{M}′,$

and we fix upon any imaging of the two aggregates, then we easily see that the following theorems hold :

[510] E. To every fundamental series in M corresponds as image a fundamental series in M′, and inversely ; to every ascending series an ascending one, and to every descending series a descending one ; to coherent fundamental series in M correspond as images coherent fundamental series in M′, and inversely.

F. If to a fundamental series in M belongs a limiting element in M, then to the corresponding fundamental series in M′ belongs a limiting element in M′, and inversely ; and these two limiting elements are images of one another in the imaging.

G. To the principal elements of M correspond as images principal elements of M′, and inversely.

If an aggregate M consists of principal elements, so that every one of its elements is a principal element, we call it an "aggregate which is dense in itself (*insichdichte Menge*)." If to every fundamental series in M there is a limiting element in M, we call M a "closed (*abgeschlossene*) aggregate." An aggregate which is both "dense in itself" and "closed" is called a "perfect aggregate." If an aggregate has one of these three predicates, every similar aggregate has the same predicate ; thus these predicates can also be ascribed to the corresponding ordinal types, and so there are "types which are dense in themselves," "closed types," "perfect types," and also "everywhere-dense types" (§ 9).

For example, η is a type which is "dense in itself," and, as we showed in § 9, it is also "everywhere-dense," but it is not "closed." The types ω and $*\omega$ have no principal elements, but $\omega+\nu$ and $\nu+*\omega$ each have a principal element, and are "closed" types. The type $\omega.3$ has two principal elements, but is not "closed"; the type $\omega.3+\nu$ has three principal elements, and is "closed."

§ 11
The Ordinal Type θ of the Linear Continuum X

We turn to the investigation of the ordinal type of the aggregate $X = \{x\}$ of all real numbers x, such that $x \geq 0$ and ≤ 1, in their natural order of precedence, so that, with any two of its elements x and x',

$$x \prec x', \quad \text{if} \quad x < x'.$$

Let the notation for this type be

(1) $$\overline{X} = \theta.$$

[511] From the elements of the theory of rational and irrational numbers we know that every fundamental series $\{x_\nu\}$ in X has a limiting element x_0 in X, and that also, inversely, every element x of X

is a limiting element of coherent fundamental series in X. Consequently X is a "perfect aggregate" and θ is a "perfect type."

But θ is not sufficiently characterized by that; besides that we must fix our attention on the following property of X. The aggregate X contains as part the aggregate R of ordinal type η investigated in § 9, and in such a way that, between any two elements x_0 and x_1 of X, elements of R lie.

We will now show that these properties, taken together, characterize the ordinal type θ of the linear continuum X in an exhaustive manner, so that we have the theorem :

If an ordered aggregate M is such that (a) it is "perfect," and (b) in it is contained an aggregate S with the cardinal number $\overline{\overline{S}} = \aleph_0$ and which bears such a relation to M that, between any two elements m_0 and m_1 of M elements of S lie, then $\overline{M} = \theta$.

Proof.—If S had a lowest or a highest element, these elements, by (b), would bear the same character as elements of M ; we could remove them from S without S losing thereby the relation to M expressed in (b). Thus, we suppose that S is without lowest or highest element, so that, by § 9, it has the ordinal type η. For since S is a part of M, between any two elements s_0 and s_1 of S other elements of S must, by (b), lie. Besides, by (b) we have $\overline{\overline{S}} = \aleph_0$. Thus the aggregates S and R are "similar" to one another.

$$S \backsim R.$$

We fix on any "imaging" of R on S, and assert that it gives a definite "imaging" of X on M in the following manner :

Let all elements of X which, at the same time, belong to the aggregate R correspond as images to those elements of M which are, at the same time, elements of S and, in the supposed imaging of R on S, correspond to the said elements of R. But if x_0 is an element of X which does not belong to R, x_0 may be regarded as a limiting element of a fundamental series $\{x_\nu\}$ contained in X, and this series can be replaced by a coherent fundamental series $\{r_{\kappa_\nu}\}$ contained in R. To this [512] corresponds as image a fundamental series $\{s_{\lambda_\nu}\}$ in S and M, which, because of (*a*), is limited by an element m_0 of M that does not belong to S (F, § 10). Let this element m_0 of M (which remains the same, by E, C, and D of § 10, if the fundamental series $\{x_\nu\}$ and $\{r_{\kappa_\nu}\}$ are replaced by others limited by the same element x_0 in X) be the image of x_0 in X. Inversely, to every element m_0 of M which does not occur in S belongs a quite definite element x_0 of X which does not belong to R and of which m_0 is the image.

In this manner a bi-univocal correspondence between X and M is set up, and we have now to show that it gives an "imaging" of these aggregates.

This is, of course, the case for those elements of X which belong to R, and for those elements of M which belong to S.   Let us compare an element r of R with an element x_0 of X which does not belong to R ; let the corresponding elements of M be s and m_0. If $r < x_0$, there is an ascending fundamental series $\{r_{\kappa_\nu}\}$, which is limited by x_0 and, from a certain ν_0 on,

$$r < r_{\kappa_\nu} \quad \text{for} \quad \nu \overline{\overline{>}} \nu_0.$$

The image of $\{r_{\kappa_\nu}\}$ in M is an ascending fundamental series $\{s_{\lambda_\nu}'\}$, which will be limited by an m_0 of M, and we have (§ 10) $s_{\lambda_\nu} < m_0$ for every ν, and $s < s_{\lambda_\nu}$ for $\nu \overline{\overline{>}} \nu_0$. Thus (§ 7) $s < m_0$.

If $r > x_0$, we conclude similarly that $s > m_0$.

Let us consider, finally, two elements x_0 and x'_0 not belonging to R and the elements m_0 and m'_0 corresponding to them in M ; then we show, by an analogous consideration, that, if $x_0 < x'_0$, then $m_0 < m'_0$.

The proof of the similarity of X and M is now finished, and we thus have

$$\overline{M} = \theta.$$

HALLE, *March* 1895.

CONTRIBUTIONS TO THE
FOUNDING OF THE THEORY OF
TRANSFINITE NUMBERS

(SECOND ARTICLE)

§ 12

Well-Ordered Aggregates

AMONG simply ordered aggregates "well-ordered aggregates" deserve a special place; their ordinal types, which we call "ordinal numbers," form the natural material for an exact definition of the higher transfinite cardinal numbers or powers,—a definition which is throughout conformable to that which was given us for the least transfinite cardinal number Aleph-zero by the system of all finite numbers ν (§ 6).

We call a simply ordered aggregate F (§ 7) "well-ordered" if its elements f ascend in a definite succession from a lowest f_1 in such a way that:

I. There is in F an element f_1 which is lowest in rank.

II. If F' is any part of F and if F has one or many elements of higher rank than all elements of F', then there is an element f' of F which follows immediately after the totality F', so that no elements in rank between f' and F' occur in F.*

In particular, to every single element f of F, if it is not the highest, follows in rank as next higher another definite element f'; this results from the condition II if for F' we put the single element f. Further, if, for example, an infinite series of consecutive elements

$$e' < e'' < e''' < \ldots < e^{(\nu)} < e^{(\nu+1)} \ldots$$

is contained in F in such a way, however, that there are also in F elements of **[208]** higher rank than all elements $e^{(\nu)}$, then, by the second condition, putting for F' the totality $\{e^{(\nu)}\}$, there must exist an element f' such that not only

$$f' > e^{(\nu)}$$

for all values of ν, but that also there is no element g in F which satisfies the two conditions

$$g < f',$$
$$g > e^{(\nu)}$$

for all values of ν.

Thus, for example, the three aggregates

$$(a_1, a_2, \ldots, a_\nu, \ldots),$$
$$(a_1, a_2, \ldots, a_\nu, \ldots, b_1, b_2 \ldots, b_\mu, \ldots),$$
$$(a_1, a_2, \ldots, a_\nu, \ldots b_1, b_2, \ldots, b_\mu, \ldots c_1, c_2, c_3),$$

where

$$a_\nu < a_{\nu+1} < b_\mu < b_{\mu+1} < c_1 < c_2 < c_3,$$

---

* This definition of "well-ordered aggregates," apart from the wording, is identical with that which was introduced in vol. xxi of the *Math. Ann.*, p. 548 (*Grundlagen einer allgemeinen Mannichfaltig-keitslehre*, p. 4). [See Section VII of the Introduction.]

are well-ordered. The two first have no highest element, the third has the highest element c_3; in the second and third b_1 immediately follows all the elements a_ν, in the third c_1 immediately follows all the elements a_ν and b_μ.

In the following we will extend the use of the signs $<$ and $>$, explained in § 7, and there used to express the ordinal relation of two elements, to groups of elements, so that the formulæ

$$M < N,$$
$$M > N$$

are the expression for the fact that in a given order all the elements of the aggregate M have a lower, or higher, respectively, rank than all elements of the aggregate N.

A. Every part F_1 of a well-ordered aggregate F has a lowest element.

Proof.—If the lowest element f_1 of F belongs to F_1, then it is also the lowest element of F_1. In the other case, let F′ be the totality of all elements of F′ which have a lower rank than all elements F_1, then, for this reason, no element of F lies between F′ and F_1. Thus, if f' follows (II) next after F′, then it belongs necessarily to F and here takes the lowest rank.

B. If a simply ordered aggregate F is such that both F and every one of its parts have a lowest element, then F is a well-ordered aggregate.

[209] *Proof.*—Since F has a lowest element, the condition I is satisfied. Let F′ be a part of F

such that there are in F one or more elements which follow F′; let F_1 be the totality of all these elements and $f′$ the lowest element of F_1, then obviously $f′$ is the element of F which follows next to F′. Consequently, the condition II is also satisfied, and therefore F is a well-ordered aggregate.

C. Every part F′ of a well-ordered aggregate F is also a well-ordered aggregate.

Proof.—By theorem A, the aggregate F′ as well as every part F″ of F′ (since it is also a part of F) has a lowest element; thus by theorem B, the aggregate F′ is well-ordered.

D. Every aggregate G which is similar to a well-ordered aggregate F is also a well-ordered aggregate.

Proof.—If M is an aggregate which has a lowest element, then, as immediately follows from the concept of similarity (§ 7), every aggregate N similar to it has a lowest element. Since, now, we are to have $G \backsim F$, and F has, since it is a well-ordered aggregate, a lowest element, the same holds of G. Thus also every part G′ of G has a lowest element; for in an imaging of G on F, to the aggregate G′ corresponds a part F′ of F as image, so that

$$G′ \backsim F′.$$

But, by theorem A, F′ has a lowest element, and therefore also G′ has. Thus, both G and every part of G have lowest elements. By theorem B, consequently, G is a well-ordered aggregate.

E. If in a well-ordered aggregate G, in place of

its elements g well-ordered aggregates are substituted in such a way that, if F_g and $F_{g'}$ are the well-ordered aggregates which occupy the places of the elements g and g' and $g \prec g'$, then also $F_g \prec F_{g'}$, then the aggregate H, arising by combination in this manner of the elements of all the aggregates F_g, is well-ordered.

Proof.—Both H and every part H_1 of H have lowest elements, and by theorem B this characterizes H as a well-ordered aggregate. For, if g_1 is the lowest element of G, the lowest element of F_{g_1} is at the same time the lowest element of H. If, further, we háve a part H_1 of H, its elements belong to definite aggregates F_g which form, when taken together, a part of the well-ordered aggregate $\{F_g\}$, which consists of the elements F_g and is similar to the aggregate G. If, say, F_{g_0} is the lowest element of this part, then the lowest element of the part of H_1 contained in F_{g_0} is at the same time the lowest element of H.

[210]   § 13

The Segments of Well-Ordered Aggregates

If f is any element of the well-ordered aggregate F which is different from the initial element f_1, then we will call the aggregate A of all elements of F which precede f a " segment (*Abschnitt*) of F," or, more fully, "the segment of F which is defined by the element f." On the other hand, the aggregate R of all the other elements of F, including f, is a "remainder of F," and, more fully, "the remainder which is determined by the element f." The aggregates A and R are, by theorem C of § 12, well-ordered, and we may, by § 8 and § 12, write :

$$(1) \qquad F = (A, R),$$
$$(2) \qquad R = (f, R'),$$
$$(3) \qquad A \prec R.$$

R' is the part of R which follows the initial element f and reduces to o if R has, besides f, no other element.

For example, in the well-ordered aggregate

$$F = (a_1, a_2, \ldots, a_\nu, \ldots b_1, b_2, \ldots, b_\mu, \ldots c_1, c_2, c_3),$$

the segment

$$(a_1, a_2)$$

and the corresponding remainder

$$(a_3, a_4, \ldots a_{\nu+2}, \ldots b_1, b_2, \ldots b_\mu, \ldots c_1, c_2, c_3)$$

are determined by the element a_3 ; the segment

$$(a_1, a_2, \ldots, a_\nu, \ldots)$$

and the corresponding remainder

$$(b_1, b_2, \ldots, b_\mu, \ldots c_1, c_2, c_3)$$

are determined by the element b_1 ; and the segment

$$(a_1, a_2, \ldots, a_\nu, \ldots b_1, b_2, \ldots, b_\mu, \ldots c_1)$$

and the corresponding segment

$$(c_2, c_3)$$

by the element c_2.

If A and A′ are two segments of F, f and $f′$ their determining elements, and

(4) $$f′ \prec f,$$

then A′ is a segment of A. We call A′ the "less," and A the "greater" segment of F:

(5) $$A′ < A.$$

Correspondingly we may say of every A of F that it is "less" than F itself:

$$A < F.$$

[211] A. If two similar well-ordered aggregates F and G are imaged on one another, then to every segment A of F corresponds a similar segment B of G, and to every segment B of G corresponds a similar segment A of F, and the elements f and g of F and G by which the corresponding segments A and B are determined also correspond to one another in the imaging.

Proof.—If we have two similar simply ordered aggregates M and N imaged on one another, m and n are two corresponding elements, and M′ is the aggregate of all elements of M which precede m and N′ is the aggregate of all elements of N which precede n, then in the imaging M′ and N′ correspond to one another. For, to every element $m′$ of M that precedes m must correspond, by § 7, an element

n' of N that precedes n, and inversely.   If we apply this general theorem to the well-ordered aggregates F and G we get what is to be proved.

B. A well-ordered aggregate F is not similar to any of its segments A.

Proof.—Let us suppose that F $\sim$ A, then we will imagine an imaging of F on A set up.   By theorem A the segment A' of A corresponds to the segment A of F, so that A' $\sim$ A.   Thus also we would have A' $\sim$ F and A' < A.   From A' would result, in the same manner, a smaller segment A'' of F, such that A'' $\sim$ F and A'' < A' ; and so on.   Thus we would obtain an infinite series

$$A > A' > A'' \ldots A^{(\nu)} > A^{(\nu+1)} \ldots$$

of segments of F, which continually become smaller and all similar to the aggregate F.   We will denote by $f, f', f'', \ldots, f^{(\nu)}, \ldots$ the elements of F which determine these segments ; then we would have

$$f > f' > f'' > \ldots > f^{(\nu)} > f^{(\nu+1)} \ldots$$

We would therefore have an infinite part

$$(f, f', f'', \ldots, f^{(\nu)}, \ldots)$$

of F in which no element takes the lowest rank. But by theorem A of § 12 such parts of F are not possible.   Thus the supposition of an imaging F on one of its segments leads to a contradiction, and consequently the aggregate F is not similar to any of its segments.

Though by theorem B a well-ordered aggregate F is not similar to any of its segments, yet, if F is infinite, there are always [212] other parts of F to which F is similar. Thus, for example, the aggregate

$$F = (a_1, a_2, \ldots, a_\nu, \ldots)$$

is similar to every one of its remainders

$$(a_{\kappa+1}, a_{\kappa+2}, \ldots, a_{\kappa+\nu}, \ldots).$$

Consequently, it is important that we can put by the side of theorem B the following :

Ç. A well-ordered aggregate F is similar to no part of any one of its segments A.

Proof.—Let us suppose that F′ is a part of a segment A of F and F′ $\curvearrowright$ F. We imagine an imaging of F on F′; then, by theorem A, to a segment A of the well-ordered aggregate F corresponds as image the segment F″ of F′; let this segment be determined by the element f' of F′. The element f' is also an element of A, and determines a segment A′ of A of which F″ is a part. The supposition of a part F′ of a segment A of F such that F′ $\curvearrowright$ F leads us consequently to a part F″ of a segment A′ of A such that F″ $\curvearrowright$ A. The same manner of conclusion gives us a part F‴ of a segment A″ of A′ such that F‴ $\curvearrowright$ A′. Proceeding thus, we get, as in the proof of theorem B, an infinite series of segments of F which continually become smaller :

$$A > A' > A'' \ldots A^{(\nu)} > A^{(\nu+1)} \ldots,$$

and thus an infinite series of elements determining
these segments:

$$f > f' > f'' \ldots f^{(\nu)} > f^{(\nu+1)} \ldots,$$

in which is no lowest element, and this is impossible
by theorem A of § 12. Thus there is no part F'
of a segment A of F such that F' $\underset{\smile}{} $ F.

D. Two different segments A and A' of a well-
ordered aggregate F are not similar to one another.

Proof.—If A' < A, then A' is a segment of the
well-ordered aggregate A, and thus, by theorem B,
cannot be similar to A.

E. Two similar well-ordered aggregates F and G
can be imaged on one another only in a single
manner.

Proof.—Let us suppose that there are two different
imagings of F on G, and let *f* be an element of F to
which in the two imagings different images *g* and *g'*
in G correspond. Let A be the segment of F that
is determined by *f*, and B and B' the segments of G
that are determined by *g* and *g'*. By theorem A,
both A $\underset{\smile}{} $ B **[213]** and A $\underset{\smile}{} $ B', and consequently
B $\underset{\smile}{} $ B', contrary to theorem D.

F. If F and G are two well-ordered aggregates,
a segment A of F can have at most one segment
B in G which is similar to it.

Proof.—If the segment A of F could have two
segments B and B' in G which were similar to it, B
and B' would be similar to one another, which is
impossible by theorem D.

G. If A and B are similar segments of two well-ordered aggregates F and G, for every smaller segment A′ < A of F there is a similar segment B′ < B of G and for every smaller segment B′ < B of G a similar segment A′ < A of F.

The proof follows from theorem A applied to the similar aggregates A and B.

H. If A and A′ are two segments of a well-ordered aggregate F, B and B′ are two segments similar to those of a well-ordered aggregate G, and A′ < A, then B′ < B.

The proof follows from the theorems F and G.

I. If a segment B of a well-ordered aggregate G is similar to no segment of a well-ordered aggregate F, then both every segment B′ > B of D and G itself are similar neither to a segment of F nor F itself.

The proof follows from theorem G.

K. If for any segment A of a well-ordered aggregate F there is a similar segment B of another well-ordered aggregate G, and also inversely, for every segment B of G a similar segment A of F, then F ⌣ G.

Proof.—We can image F and G on one another according to the following law : Let the lowest element f_1 of F correspond to the lowest element g_1 of G. If $f > f_1$ is any other element of F, it determines a segment A of F. To this segment belongs by supposition a definite similar segment B of G, and let the element g of G which determines the segment B be the image of F. And if g is any element of G that follows g_1, it determines a segment B of G, to which by supposition a similar segment A of F belongs. Let the element f which determines this segment A be the image of g. It easily follows that the bi-univocal correspondence of F and G defined in this manner is an imaging in the sense of § 7. For if f and f' are any two elements of F, g and g' [214] the corresponding elements of G, A and A' the segments determined by f and f', B and B' those determined by g and g', and if, say,

$$f' < f,$$
then
$$A' < A.$$

By theorem H, then, we have

$$B' < B,$$
and consequently
$$g' < g.$$

L. If for every segment A of a well-ordered aggregate F there is a similar segment B of another well-ordered aggregate G, but if, on the other hand, there is at least one segment of G for which there is no similar segment of F, then there exists a definite segment B_1 of G such that $B_1 \backsim F$.

Proof.—Consider the totality of segments of G for which there are no similar segments in F. Amongst them there must be a least segment which we will call B_1. This follows from the fact that, by theorem A of § 12, the aggregate of all the elements determining these segments has a lowest element; the segment B_1 of G determined by that element is the least of that totality. By theorem I, every segment of G which is greater than B_1 is such that no segment similar to it is present in F. Thus the segments B of G which correspond to similar segments of F must all be less than B_1, and to every segment $B < B_1$ belongs a similar segment A of F, because B_1 is the least segment of G among those to which no similar segments in F correspond. Thus, for every segment A of F there is a similar segment B of B_1, and for every segment B of B_1 there is a similar segment A of F. By theorem K, we thus have

$$F \backsim B_1.$$

M. If the well-ordered aggregate G has at least one segment for which there is no similar segment in the well-ordered aggregate F, then every segment A of F must have a segment B similar to it in G.

Proof.—Let B_1 be the least of all those segments of G for which there are no similar segments in F.* If there were segments in F for which there were no corresponding segments in G, amongst these, one, which we will call A_1, would be the least. For every segment of A_1 would then exist a similar segment of B_1, and also for every segment of B_1 a similar segment of A_1. Thus, by theorem K, we would have

$$B_1 \backsim A_1.$$

[215] But this contradicts the datum that for B_1 there is no similar segment of F. Consequently, there cannot be in F a segment to which a similar segment in G does not correspond.

* See the above proof of L.

N. If F and G are any two well-ordered aggregates, then either :

(*a*) F and G are similar to one another, or

(*b*) there is a definite segment B_1 of G to which F is similar, or

(*c*) there is a definite segment A_1 of F to which G is similar ;

and each of these three cases excludes the two others.

Proof.—The relation of F to G can be any one of the three :

(*a*) To every segment A of F there belongs a similar segment B of G, and inversely, to every segment B of G belongs a similar one A of F ;

(*b*) To every segment A of F belongs a similar segment B of G, but there is at least one segment of G to which no similar segment in F corresponds;

(*c*) To every segment B of G belongs a similar segment A of F, but there is at least one segment of F to which no similar segment in G corresponds.

The case that there is both a segment of F to which no similar segment in G corresponds and a segment of G to which no similar segment in F corresponds is not possible ; it is excluded by theorem M.

By theorem K, in the first case we have

$$F \underset{\sim}{} G.$$

In the second case there is, by theorem L, a definite segment B_1 of B such that

$$B_1 \underset{\sim}{} F ;$$

and in the third case there is a definite segment A_1 of F such that

$$A_1 \backsim G.$$

We cannot have $F \backsim G$ and $F \backsim B_1$ simultaneously, for then we would have $G \backsim B_1$, contrary to theorem B ; and, for the same reason, we cannot have both $F \backsim G$ and $G \backsim A_1$. Also it is impossible that both $F \backsim B_1$ and $G \backsim A_1$, for, by theorem A, from $F \backsim B_1$ would follow the existence of a segment B'_1 of B_1 such that $A_1 \backsim B'_1$. Thus we would have $G \backsim B'_1$, contrary to theorem B.

O. If a part F' of a well-ordered aggregate F is not similar to any segment of F, it is similar to F itself.

Proof.—By theorem C of § 12, F' is a well-ordered aggregate. If F' were similar neither to a segment of F nor to F itself, there would be, by theorem N, a segment F'_1 of F' which is similar to F. But F'_1 is a part of that segment A of F which [216] is determined by the same element as the segment F'_1 of F'. Thus the aggregate F would have to be similar to a part of one of its segments, and this contradicts the theorem C.

§ 14

The Ordinal Numbers of Well-Ordered Aggregates

By § 7, every simply ordered aggregate M has a definite ordinal type $\overline{M}$; this type is the general concept which results from M if we abstract from the nature of its elements while retaining their order of precedence, so that out of them proceed units (*Einsen*) which stand in a definite relation of precedence to one another.   All aggregates which are similar to one another, and only such, have one and the same ordinal type.   We call the ordinal type of a well-ordered aggregate F its "ordinal number."

If a and β are any two ordinal numbers, one can stand to the other in one of three possible relations. For if F and G are two well-ordered aggregates such that

$$\overline{F} = a, \quad \overline{G} = \beta,$$

then, by theorem N of § 13, three mutually exclusive cases are possible :

(*a*) $\qquad\qquad$ F $\sim$ G ;

(*b*) There is a definite segment B_1 of G such that

$$F \sim B_1 ;$$

(*c*) There is a definite segment A_1 of F such that

$$G \sim A_1.$$

As we easily see, each of these cases still subsists if F and G are replaced by aggregates respectively similar to them.   Accordingly, we have to do with three mutually exclusive relations of the types a and β to one another.   In the first case $a = \beta$; in the second we say that $a < \beta$; in the third we say that $a > \beta$.   Thus we have the theorem :

A. If a and β are any two ordinal numbers, we have either $a=\beta$ or $a<\beta$ or $a>\beta$.

From the definition of minority and majority follows easily :

B. If we have three ordinal numbers a, β, γ, and if $a<\beta$ and $\beta<\gamma$, then $a<\gamma$.

Thus the ordinal numbers form, when arranged in order of magnitude, a simply ordered aggregate ; it will appear later that it is a well-ordered aggregate.

[217] The operations of addition and multiplication of the ordinal types of any simply ordered aggregates, defined in § 8, are, of course, applicable to the ordinal numbers. If $a=\overline{F}$ and $\beta=\overline{G}$, where F and G are two well-ordered aggregates, then

$$(1) \qquad a+\beta=(\overline{F, G}).$$

The aggregate of union (F, G) is obviously a well-ordered aggregate too ; thus we have the theorem :

C. The sum of two ordinal numbers is also an ordinal number.

In the sum $a+\beta$, a is called the "augend" and β the "addend."

Since F is a segment of (F, G), we have always

$$(2) \qquad a<a+\beta.$$

On the other hand, G is not a segment but a remainder of (F, G), and may thus, as we saw in § 13, be similar to the aggregate (F, G). If this is not the case, G is, by theorem O of § 13, similar to a segment of (F, G).   Thus

(3) $$\beta \leqq \alpha + \beta.$$

Consequently we have :

D. The sum of the two ordinal numbers is always greater than the augend, but greater than or equal to the addend.   If we have $\alpha + \beta = \alpha + \gamma$, we always have $\beta = \gamma$.

In general $\alpha + \beta$ and $\beta + \alpha$ are not equal.   On the other hand, we have, if γ is a third ordinal number,

(4) $$(\alpha + \beta) + \gamma = \alpha + (\beta + \gamma).$$

That is to say :

E. In the addition of ordinal numbers the associative law always holds.

If we substitute for every element g of the aggregate G of type β an aggregate F_g of type α, we get, by theorem E of § 12, a well-ordered aggregate H whose type is completely determined by the types α and β and will be called the product $\alpha . \beta$:

(5) $$\overline{F}_g = \alpha,$$

(6) $$\alpha . \beta = \overline{H}.$$

F. The product of two ordinal numbers is also an ordinal number.

In the product $\alpha . \beta$, α is called the "multiplicand" and β the "multiplier."

In general $\alpha . \beta$ and $\beta . \alpha$ are not equal.   But we have (§ 8)

(7) $$(a \cdot \beta) \cdot \gamma = a \cdot (\beta \cdot \gamma).$$

That is to say :

[218] G. In the multiplication of ordinal numbers the associative law holds.

The distributive law is valid, in general (§ 8), only in the following form :

(8) $$a \cdot (\beta + \gamma) = a \cdot \beta + a \cdot \gamma.$$

With reference to the magnitude of the product, the following theorem, as we easily see, holds :

H. If the multiplier is greater than 1, the product of two ordinal numbers is always greater than the multiplicand, but greater than or equal to the multiplier. If we have $a \cdot \beta = a \cdot \gamma$, then it always follows that $\beta = \gamma$.

On the other hand, we evidently have

(9) $$a \cdot 1 = 1 \cdot a = a.$$

We have now to consider the operation of subtraction. If a and β are two ordinal numbers, and a is less than β, there always exists a definite ordinal number which we will call $\beta - a$, which satisfies the equation

(10) $$a + (\beta - a) = \beta.$$

For if $\overline{G} = \beta$, G has a segment B such that $\overline{B} = a$; we call the corresponding remainder S, and have

$$G = (B, S),$$
$$\beta = a + \overline{S} ;$$

and therefore

(11) $$\beta - \alpha = \overline{S}.$$

The determinateness of $\beta - \alpha$ appears clearly from the fact that the segment B of G is a completely definite one (theorem D of § 13), and consequently also S is uniquely given.

We emphasize the following formulæ, which follow from (4), (8), and (10):

(12) $$(\gamma + \beta) - (\gamma + \alpha) = \beta - \alpha,$$
(13) $$\gamma(\beta - \alpha) = \gamma\beta - \gamma\alpha.$$

It is important to reflect that an infinity of ordinal numbers can be summed so that their sum is a definite ordinal number which depends on the sequence of the summands. If

$$\beta_1, .\beta_2, \ldots, \beta_\nu, \ldots$$

is any simply infinite series of ordinal numbers, and we have

(14) $$\beta_\nu = \overline{G}_\nu,$$

[219] then, by theorem E of § 12,

(15) $$G = (G_1, G_2, \ldots, G_\nu, \ldots)$$

is also a well-ordered aggregate whose ordinal number represents the sum of the numbers β_ν. We have, then,

(16) $$\beta_1 + \beta_2 + \ldots + \beta_\nu + \ldots = \overline{G} = \beta,$$

and, as we easily see from the definition of a product, we always have

(17) $\quad \gamma \cdot (\beta_1 + \beta_2 + \ldots + \beta_\nu + \ldots)$
$$= \gamma \cdot \beta_1 + \gamma \cdot \beta_2 + \ldots + \gamma \cdot \beta_\nu + \ldots$$

If we put

(18) $\qquad a_\nu = \beta_1 + \beta_2 + \ldots + \beta_\nu,$

then

(19) $\qquad a_\nu = \overline{(G_1, \ G_2, \ \ldots \ G_\nu)}.$

We have

(20) $\qquad\qquad a_{\nu+1} > a_\nu,$

and, by (10), we can express the numbers β_ν by the numbers a_ν as follows :

(21) $\qquad \beta_1 = a_1 ; \quad \beta_{\nu+1} = a_{\nu+1} - a_\nu.$

The series

$$a_1, \ a_2, \ \ldots, \ a_\nu, \ \ldots$$

thus represents *any* infinite series of ordinal numbers which satisfy the condition (20); we will call it a "fundamental series" of ordinal numbers (§ 10). Between it and β subsists a relation which can be expressed in the following manner :

(*a*) The number β is greater than a_ν for every ν, because the aggregate $(G_1, G_2, \ldots, G_\nu)$, whose ordinal number is a_ν, is a segment of the aggregate G which has the ordinal number β ;

(*b*) If β' is any ordinal number less than β, then, from a certain ν onwards, we always have

$$a_\nu > \beta'.$$

For, since $\beta' < \beta$, there is a segment B' of the

aggregate G which is of type β'. The element of G which determines this segment must belong to one of the parts G_ν; we will call this part G_{ν_0}. But then B′ is also a segment of $(G_1, G_2, \ldots, G_{\nu_0})$, and consequently $\beta' < a_{\nu_0}$. Thus

$$a_\nu > \beta'$$

for $\nu \geqq \nu_0$.

Thus β is the ordinal number which follows next in order of magnitude after all the numbers a_ν; accordingly we will call it the "limit" (*Grenze*) of the numbers a_ν for increasing ν and denote it by Lim a_ν, so that, by (16) and (21):

$$(22) \quad \operatorname*{Lim}_{\nu} a_\nu = a_1 + (a_2 - a_1) + \ldots + (a_{\nu+1} - a_\nu) + \ldots$$

[220] We may express what precedes in the following theorem :

1. To every fundamental series $\{a_\nu\}$ of ordinal numbers belongs an ordinal number $\operatorname*{Lim}_{\nu} a_\nu$ which follows next, in order of magnitude, after all the numbers a_ν; it is represented by the formula (22).

If by γ we understand any constant ordinal number, we easily prove, by the aid of the formulæ (12), (13), and (17), the theorems contained in the formulæ :

$$(23) \qquad \operatorname*{Lim}_{\nu} (\gamma + a_\nu) = \gamma + \operatorname*{Lim}_{\nu} a_\nu ;$$

$$(24) \qquad \operatorname*{Lim}_{\nu} \gamma . a_\nu = \gamma . \operatorname*{Lim}_{\nu} a_\nu.$$

We have already mentioned in § 7 that all simply

ordered aggregates of given finite cardinal number ν have one and the same ordinal type. This may be proved here as follows. Every simply ordered aggregate of finite cardinal number is a well-ordered aggregate ; for it, and every one of its parts, must have a lowest element,—and this, by theorem B of § 12, characterizes it as a well-ordered aggregate. The types of finite simply ordered aggregates are thus none other than finite ordinal numbers. But two different ordinal numbers α and β cannot belong to the same finite cardinal number ν. For if, say, $\alpha < \beta$ and $\overline{G} = \beta$, then, as we know, there exists a segment B of G such that $\overline{B} = \alpha$. Thus the aggregate G and its part B would have the same finite cardinal number ν. But this, by theorem C of § 6, is impossible. Thus the finite ordinal numbers coincide in their properties with the finite cardinal numbers.

The case is quite different with the transfinite ordinal numbers ; to one and the same transfinite cardinal number $\mathfrak{a}$ belong an infinity of ordinal numbers which form a unitary and connected system. We will call this system the "number-class $Z(\mathfrak{a})$," and it is a part of the class of types $[\mathfrak{a}]$ of § 7. The next object of our consideration is the number-class $Z(\aleph_0)$, which we will call "the second number-class." For in this connexion we understand by "the first number-class" the totality $\{\nu\}$ of finite ordinal numbers.

§ 15

The Numbers of the Second Number-Class $Z(\aleph_0)$

The second number-class $Z(\aleph_0)$ is the totality $\{\alpha\}$ of ordinal types α of well-ordered aggregates of the cardinal number $\aleph_0$ (§ 6).

A. The second number-class has a least number $\omega = \text{Lim } \nu$.

Proof.—By ω we understand the type of the well-ordered aggregate

(1) $$F_0 = (f_1, \, f_2, \, \ldots, \, f_\nu, \, \ldots),$$

where ν runs through all finite ordinal numbers and

(2) $$f_\nu \prec f_{\nu+1}.$$

Therefore (§ 7)

(3) $$\omega = \overline{F}_0,$$

and (§ 6)

(4) $$\overline{\omega} = \aleph_0.$$

Thus ω is a number of the second number-class, and indeed the least. For if γ is any ordinal number less than ω, it must (§ 14) be the type of a segment of F_0. But F_0 has only segments

$$A = (f_1, \, f_2, \, \ldots, \, f_\nu),$$

with *finite* ordinal number ν. Thus $\gamma = \nu$. Therefore there are no transfinite ordinal numbers which are less than ω, and thus ω is the least of them. By the definition of $\text{Lim } a_\nu$ given in § 14, we obviously have $\omega = \text{Lim } \nu$.

B. If a is any number of the second number-class, the number $a + 1$ follows it as the next greater number of the same number-class.

Proof.—Let F be a well-ordered aggregate of the type a and of the cardinal number $\aleph_0$:

(5) $$\overline{F} = a,$$

(6) $$\overline{a} = \aleph_0.$$

We have, where by g is understood a new element,

(7) $$a + 1 = (\overline{F, g}).$$

Since F is a segment of (F, g), we have

(8) $$a + 1 > a.$$

We also have

$$\overline{a + 1} = \overline{a} + 1 = \aleph_0 + 1 = \aleph_0 \ (\S\ 6).$$

Therefore the number $a + 1$ belongs to the second number-class. Between a and $a + 1$ there are no ordinal numbers ; for every number γ **[222]** which is less than $a + 1$ corresponds, as type, to a segment of (F, g), and such a segment can only be either F or a segment of F. Therefore γ is either equal to or less than a.

C. If $a_1, a_2, \ldots, a_\nu, \ldots$ is any fundamental series of numbers of the first or second number-class, then the number $\underset{\nu}{\text{Lim }} a_\nu$ ($\S$ 14) following them next in order of magnitude belongs to the second number-class.

Proof.—By $\S$ 14 there results from the fundamental series $\{a_\nu\}$ the number $\operatorname*{Lim}_\nu a_\nu$ if we set up another series $\beta_1,\ \beta_2,\ \ldots,\ \beta_\nu,\ \ldots$, where

$$\beta_1 = a_1,\ \beta_2 = a_2 - a_1,\ \ldots,\ \beta_{\nu+1} = a_{\nu+1} - a_\nu,\ \ldots$$

If, then, $G_1,\ G_2,\ \ldots,\ G_\nu,\ \ldots$ are well-ordered aggregates such that

$$\overline{G}_\nu = \beta_\nu,$$

then also

$$G = (G_1,\ G_2,\ \ldots,\ G_\nu,\ \ldots)$$

is a well-ordered aggregate and

$$\operatorname*{Lim}_\nu a_\nu = \overline{G}.$$

It only remains to prove that

$$\overline{\overline{G}} = \aleph_0.$$

Since the numbers $\beta_1,\ \beta_2,\ \ldots,\ \beta_\nu,\ \ldots$ belong to the first or second number-class, we have

$$\overline{\overline{G}}_\nu \leqq \aleph_0,$$

and thus

$$\overline{\overline{G}} \leqq \aleph_0 \cdot \aleph_0 = \aleph_0.$$

But, in any case, G is a transfinite aggregate, and so the case $\overline{\overline{G}} < \aleph_0$ is excluded.

We will call two fundamental series $\{a_\nu\}$ and $\{a'_\nu\}$ of numbers of the first or second number-class (§ 10) "coherent," in signs :

$$(9) \qquad \{a_\nu\}\ \|\ \{a'_\nu\},$$

if for every ν there are finite numbers λ_0 and μ_0 such that

$$(10) \qquad a'_\lambda > a_\nu, \quad \lambda \geqq \lambda_0,$$

and

(11) $a_\mu > a'_\nu, \quad \mu \geq \mu_0.$

[223] D. The limiting numbers $\operatorname{Lim}_\nu a_\nu$ and $\operatorname{Lim}_\nu a'_\nu$ belonging respectively to two fundamental series $\{a_\nu\}$ and $\{a'_\nu\}$ are equal when, and only when, $\{a_\nu\} \parallel \{a'_\nu\}$.

Proof. — For the sake of shortness we put $\operatorname{Lim}_\nu a_\nu = \beta$, $\operatorname{Lim}_\nu a'_\nu = \gamma$. We will first suppose that $\{a_\nu\} \parallel \{a'_\nu\}$; then we assert that $\beta = \gamma$. For if β were not equal to γ, one of these two numbers would have to be the smaller. Suppose that $\beta < \gamma$. From a certain ν onwards we would have $a'_\nu > \beta$ (§ 14), and consequently, by (11), from a certain μ onwards we would have $a_\mu > \beta$. But this is impossible because $\beta = \operatorname{Lim}_\nu a_\nu$. Thus for all μ's we have $a_\mu < \beta$.

If, inversely, we suppose that $\beta = \gamma$, then, because $a_\nu < \gamma$, we must conclude that, from a certain λ onwards, $a'_\lambda > a_\nu$, and, because $a'_\nu < \beta$, we must conclude that, from a certain μ onwards, $a_\mu > a'_\nu$. That is to say, $\{a_\nu\} \parallel \{a'_\nu\}$.

E. If a is any number of the second number-class and ν_0 any finite ordinal number, we have $\nu_0 + a = a$, and consequently also $a - \nu_0 = a$.

Proof. — We will first of all convince ourselves of the correctness of the theorem when $a = \omega$. We have

$$\omega = (\overline{f_1, f_2, \ldots, f_\nu, \ldots}),$$
$$\nu_0 = \overline{(g_1, g_2, \ldots g_{\nu_0})},$$

and consequently

$$\nu_0 + \omega = \overline{(g_1, g_2, \ldots g_{\nu_0}, f_1, f_2, \ldots, f_\nu, \ldots)} = \omega.$$

But if $a > \omega$, we have

$$a = \omega + (a - \omega),$$

$$\nu_0 + a = (\nu_0 + \omega) + (a - \omega) = \omega + (a - \omega) = a.$$

F. If ν_0 is any finite ordinal number, we have $\nu_0 . \omega = \omega$.

Proof.—In order to obtain an aggregate of the type $\nu_0 . \omega$ we have to substitute for the single elements f_ν of the aggregate $(f_1, f_2, \ldots, f_\nu, \ldots)$ aggregates $(g_{\nu, 1}, g_{\nu, 2}, \ldots, g_{\nu, \nu_0})$ of the type ν_0. We thus obtain the aggregate

$$(g_{1, 1}, g_{1, 2}, \ldots, g_{1, \nu_0}, g_{2, 1}, \ldots, g_{2, \nu_0}, \ldots, g_{\nu, 1},$$
$$g_{\nu, 2}, \ldots, g_{\nu, \nu_0}, \ldots),$$

which is obviously similar to the aggregate $\{f_\nu\}$. Consequently

$$\nu_0 . \omega = \omega.$$

The same result is obtained more shortly as follows. By (24) of § 14 we have, since $\omega = \operatorname{Lim}_\nu \nu$,

$$\nu_0 \omega = \operatorname{Lim}_\nu \nu_0 \nu.$$

On the other hand,

$$\{\nu_0 \nu\} \parallel \{\nu\},$$

and consequently

$$\operatorname{Lim}_\nu \nu_0 \nu = \operatorname{Lim}_\nu \nu = \omega;$$

so that

$$\nu_0 \omega = \omega.$$

[224] G. We have always

$$(a+\nu_0)\omega = a\omega,$$

where a is a number of the second number-class and ν_0 a number of the first number-class.

Proof.—We have

$$\operatorname*{Lim}_{\nu} \nu = \omega.$$

By (24) of § 14 we have, consequently,

$$(a+\nu_0)\omega = \operatorname*{Lim}_{\nu} (a+\nu_0)\nu.$$

But

$$(a+\nu_0)\nu = \overbrace{(a+\nu_0)}^{1} + \overbrace{(a+\nu_0)}^{2} + \ldots + \overbrace{(a+\nu_0)}^{\nu}$$

$$= a + \overbrace{(\nu_0+a)}^{1} + \overbrace{(\nu_0+a)}^{2} \ldots \overbrace{(\nu_0+a)}^{\nu-1} + \nu_0$$

$$= \overbrace{a+a}^{1\ 2} + \ldots + \overbrace{a}^{\nu} + \nu_0$$

$$= a\nu + \nu_0.$$

Now we have, as is easy to see,

$$\{a\nu+\nu_0\} \parallel \{a\nu\},$$

and consequently

$$\operatorname*{Lim}_{\nu} (a+\nu_0)\nu = \operatorname*{Lim}_{\nu} (a\nu+\nu_0) = \operatorname*{Lim}_{\nu} a\nu = a\omega.$$

H. If a is any number of the second number-class, then the totality $\{a'\}$ of numbers a' of the first and second number-classes which are less than a form, in their order of magnitude, a well-ordered aggregate of type a.

Proof.—Let F be a well-ordered aggregate such that $\overline{F} = \alpha$, and let f_1 be the lowest element of F. If α' is any ordinal number which is less than α, then, by § 14, there is a definite segment A' of F such that

$$\overline{A'} = \alpha',$$

and inversely every segment A' determines by its type $\overline{A'} = \alpha'$ a number $\alpha' < \alpha$ of the first or second number-class. For, since $\overline{\overline{F}} = \aleph_0$, $\overline{\overline{A'}}$ can only be either a finite cardinal number or $\aleph_0$. The segment A' is determined by an element $f' > f_1$ of F, and inversely every element $f' > f_1$ of F determines a segment A' of F. If f' and f'' are two elements of F which follow f_1 in rank, A' and A'' are the segments of F determined by them, α' and α'' are their ordinal types, and, say $f' < f''$, then, by § 13, A' < A'' and consequently $\alpha' < \alpha''$. **[225]** If, then, we put F $= (f_1, $ F'$)$, we obtain, when we make the element f' of F' correspond to the element α' of $\{\alpha'\}$, an imaging of these two aggregates. Thus we have

$$\overline{\{\alpha'\}} = \overline{F'}.$$

But $\overline{F'} = \alpha - 1$, and, by theorem E, $\alpha - 1 = \alpha$. Consequently

$$\overline{\{\alpha'\}} = \alpha.$$

Since $\overline{a} = \aleph_0$, we also have $\overline{\overline{\{\alpha'\}}} = \aleph_0$; thus we have the theorems :

I. The aggregate $\{\alpha'\}$ of numbers α' of the first and second number-classes which are smaller than a number a of the second number-class has the cardinal number $\aleph_0$.

K. Every number a of the second number-class is either such that (a) it arises out of the next smaller number a_{-1} by the addition of 1 :

$$a = a_{-1} + 1,$$

or (b) there is a fundamental series $\{a_\nu\}$ of numbers of the first or second number-class such that

$$a = \underset{\nu}{\mathrm{Lim}}\ a_\nu.$$

Proof.—Let $a = \overline{F}$. If F has an element g which is highest in rank, we have $F = (A,\ g)$, where A is the segment of F which is determined by g. We have then the first case, namely,

$$a = \overline{A} + 1 = a_{-1} + 1.$$

There exists, therefore, a next smaller number which is that called a_1.

But if F has no highest element, consider the totality $\{a'\}$ of numbers of the first and second number-classes which are smaller than a. By theorem H, the aggregate $\{a'\}$, arranged in order of magnitude, is similar to the aggregate F ; among the numbers a', consequently, none is greatest. By theorem I, the aggregate $\{a'\}$ can be brought into the form $\{a'_\nu\}$ of a simply infinite series. If we set out from a'_1, the next following elements a'_2, a'_3, . . . in this order, which is different from the order of magnitude, will, in general, be smaller than a'_1 ; but in every case, in the further course of the process, terms will occur which are greater than a'_1; for a'_1 cannot be greater than all other terms, because among the numbers $\{a'_\nu\}$ there is no greatest. Let that number a'_ν which has the least index of those greater than a'_1 be a'_{ρ_2}. Similarly, let a'_{ρ_3} be that number of the series $\{a'_\nu\}$ which has the least index of those which are greater than a'_{ρ_2}. By proceeding in this way, we get an infinite series of increasing numbers, a fundamental series in fact,

$$a'_1, \ a'_{\rho_2}, \ a'_{\rho_3}, \ \ldots, \ a'_{\rho_\nu}, \ \ldots$$

[226] We have

$$1 < \rho_2 < \rho_3 < \ldots < \rho_\nu < \rho_{\nu+1} \; \ldots,$$
$$a'_1 < a'_{\rho_2} < a'_{\rho_3} < \ldots < a'_{\rho_\nu} < a'_{\rho_{\nu+1}} \ldots,$$
$$a'_\mu < a'_{\rho_\nu} \quad \text{always if} \quad \mu < \rho'_\nu;$$

and since obviously $\nu \overline{\overline{<}} \rho_\nu$, we always have

$$a'_\nu \leqq a'_{\rho_\nu}.$$

Hence we see that every number a'_ν, and consequently every number $a' < a$, is exceeded by numbers a'_{ρ_ν} for sufficiently great values of ν. But a is the number which, in respect of magnitude, immediately follows all the numbers a', and consequently is also the next greater number with respect to all a'_{ρ_ν}. If, therefore, we put $a'_1 = a_1$, $a_{\rho_{\nu+1}} = a_{\nu+1}$, we have

$$a = \operatorname*{Lim}_\nu a_\nu.$$

From the theorems B, C, . . ., K it is evident that the numbers of the second number-class result from smaller numbers in two ways. Some numbers, which we call "numbers of the first kind (*Art*)," are got from a next smaller number a_{-1} by addition of 1 according to the formula

$$a = a_{-1} + 1 ;$$

The other numbers, which we call "numbers of the second kind," are such that for any one of them there is not a next smaller number a_{-1}, but they arise from fundamental series $\{a_\nu\}$ as limiting numbers according to the formula

$$a = \operatorname*{Lim}_\nu a_\nu.$$

Here a is the number which follows next in order of magnitude to all the numbers a_ν.

We call these two ways in which greater numbers proceed out of smaller ones "the first and the second principle of generation of numbers of the second number-class." *

§ 16

The Power of the Second Number-Class is equal to the Second Greatest Transfinite Cardinal Number Aleph-One

Before we turn to the more detailed considerations in the following paragraphs of the numbers of the second number-class and of the laws which rule them, we will answer the question as to the

* [*Cf.* Section VII of the Introduction.]

cardinal number which is possessed by the aggregate $Z(\aleph_0) = \{\alpha\}$ of all these numbers.

[227] A. The totality $\{\alpha\}$ of all numbers α of the second number-class forms, when arranged in order of magnitude, a well-ordered aggregate.

Proof.—If we denote by A_α the totality of numbers of the second number-class which are smaller than a given number α, arranged in order of magnitude, then A_α is a well-ordered aggregate of type $\alpha - \omega$. This results from theorem H of § 14. The aggregate of numbers α' of the first and second number-class which was there denoted by $\{\alpha'\}$, is compounded out of $\{\nu\}$ and A_α, so that

$$\{\alpha'\} = (\{\nu\},\ A_\alpha).$$

Thus

$$\overline{\{\alpha'\}} = \overline{\{\nu\}} + \overline{A_\alpha}\ ;$$

and since

$$\overline{\{\alpha'\}} = \alpha, \quad \overline{\{\nu\}} = \omega,$$

we have

$$\overline{A_\alpha} = \alpha - \omega.$$

Let J be any part of $\{\alpha\}$ such that there are numbers in $\{\alpha\}$ which are greater than all the numbers of J. Let, say, α be one of these numbers. Then J is also a part of A_{α_0+1}, and indeed such a part that at least the number α_0 of A_{α_0+1} is greater than all the numbers of J. Since A_{α_0+1} is a well-ordered aggregate, by § 12 a number α' of A_{α_0+1}, and therefore also of $\{\alpha\}$, must follow next to all the numbers of J. Thus the condition II of § 12 is fulfilled in the case of $\{a\}$; the condition I of § 12 is also fulfilled because $\{a\}$ has the least number ω.

Now, if we apply to the well-ordered aggregate $\{a\}$ the theorems A and C of § 12, we get the following theorems :

B. Every totality of different numbers of the first and second number-classes has a least number.

C. Every totality of different numbers of the first and second number-classes arranged in their order of magnitude forms a well-ordered aggregate.

We will now show that the power of the second number-class is different from that of the first, which is $\aleph_0$.

D. The power of the totality $\{a\}$ of all numbers a of the second number-class is not equal to $\aleph_0$.

Proof.—If $\overline{\{a\}}$ were equal to $\aleph_0$, we could bring the totality $\{a\}$ into the form of a simply infinite series

$$\gamma_1, \gamma_2, \ldots, \gamma_\nu, \ldots$$

such that $\{\gamma_\nu\}$ would represent the totality of numbers of the second [228] number-class in an order which is different from the order of magnitude, and $\{\gamma_\nu\}$ would contain, like $\{a\}$, no greatest number.

Starting from γ_1, let γ_{ρ_2} be the term of the series which has the least index of those greater than γ_1, γ_{ρ_3} the term which has the least index of those greater than γ_{ρ_2}, and so on. We get an infinite series of increasing numbers,

$$\gamma_1, \gamma_{\rho_2}, \ldots, \gamma_{\rho_\nu}, \ldots,$$

such that

$$1 < \rho_2 < \rho_3 \ldots < \rho_\nu < \rho_{\nu+1} < \ldots,$$
$$\gamma_1 < \gamma_{\rho_2} < \gamma_{\rho_3} \ldots < \gamma_{\rho_\nu} < \gamma_{\rho_{\nu+1}} < \ldots,$$
$$\gamma_\nu \leqq \gamma_{\rho_\nu}.$$

By theorem C of § 15, there would be a definite number δ of the second number-class, namely,

$$\delta = \operatorname*{Lim}_\nu \gamma_{\rho_\nu},$$

which is greater than all numbers γ_{ρ_ν}. Consequently we would have

$$\delta > \gamma_\nu$$

for every ν. But $\{\gamma_\nu\}$ contains *all* numbers of the second number-class, and consequently also the number δ; thus we would have, for a definite ν_0,

$$\delta = \gamma_{\nu_0},$$

which equation is inconsistent with the relation $\delta > \gamma_{\nu_0}$. The supposition $\overline{\{a\}} = \aleph_0$ consequently leads to a contradiction.

E. Any totality $\{\beta\}$ of different numbers β of the second number-class has, if it is infinite, either the cardinal number $\aleph_0$ or the cardinal number $\overline{\{a\}}$ of the second number-class.

Proof.—The aggregate $\{\beta\}$, when arranged in its order of magnitude, is, since it is a part of the well-ordered aggregate $\{a\}$, by theorem O of § 13, similar either to a segment A_{a_0}, which is the totality of all numbers of the same number-class which are less than a_0, arranged in their order of magnitude, or to the totality $\{a\}$ itself. As was shown in the proof of theorem A, we have

$$\overline{A}_{a_0} = a_0 - \omega.$$

Thus we have either $\overline{\{\beta\}} = a_0 - \omega$ or $\overline{\{\beta\}} = \overline{\{a\}}$, and consequently $\overline{\{\beta\}}$ is either equal to $\overline{a_0 - \omega}$ or $\overline{\{a\}}$. But $\overline{a_0 - \omega}$ is either a finite cardinal number or is equal to $\aleph_0$ (theorem I of § 15). The first case is here excluded because $\{\beta\}$ is supposed to be an infinite aggregate. Thus the cardinal number $\overline{\overline{\{\beta\}}}$ is either equal to $\aleph_0$ or $\overline{\overline{\{a\}}}$.

F. The power of the second number-class $\{a\}$ is the second greatest transfinite cardinal number Aleph-one.

[229] *Proof.*—There is no cardinal number a which is greater than $\aleph_0$ and less than $\overline{\overline{\{a\}}}$. For if not, there would have to be, by § 2, an infinite part $\{\beta\}$ of $\{a\}$ such that $\overline{\overline{\{\beta\}}} = a$. But by the theorem E just proved, the part $\{\beta\}$ has either the cardinal number $\aleph_0$ or the cardinal number $\overline{\overline{\{a\}}}$. Thus the cardinal number $\overline{\overline{\{a\}}}$ is necessarily the cardinal number which immediately follows $\aleph_0$ in magnitude; we call this new cardinal number $\aleph_1$.

In the second number-class $Z(\aleph_0)$ we possess, consequently, the natural representative for the second greatest transfinite cardinal number Aleph-one.

§ 17

The Numbers of the Form $\omega^\mu \nu_0 + \omega^{\mu-1}\nu_1 + \ldots + \nu_\mu$.

It is convenient to make ourselves familiar, in the first place, with those numbers of $Z(\aleph_0)$ which are whole algebraic functions of finite degree of ω. Every such number can be brought—and brought in only one way—into the form

$$(1) \qquad \phi = \omega^\mu \nu_0 + \omega^{\mu-1}\nu_1 + \ldots + \nu_\mu,$$

where μ, ν_0 are finite and different from zero, but $\nu_1, \nu_2, \ldots, \nu_\mu$ may be zero. This rests on the fact that

$$(2) \qquad \omega^{\mu'}\nu' + \omega^\mu \nu = \omega^\mu \nu,$$

if $\mu' < \mu$ and $\nu > 0$, $\nu' > 0$. For, by (8) of § 14, we have

$$\omega^{\mu'}\nu' + \omega^\mu \nu = \omega^{\mu'}(\nu' + \omega^{\mu-\mu'}\nu),$$

and, by theorem E of § 15,

$$\nu' + \omega^{\mu-\mu'}\nu = \omega^{\mu-\mu'}\nu.$$

Thus, in an aggregate of the form

$$\ldots + \omega^{\mu'}\nu' + \omega^\mu \nu + \ldots,$$

all those terms which are followed towards the right by terms of higher degree in ω may be omitted. This method may be continued until the form given in (1) is reached. We will also emphasize that

$$(3) \qquad \omega^\mu \nu + \omega^\mu \nu' = \omega^\mu(\nu + \nu').$$

Compare, now, the number ϕ with a number ψ of the same kind:

$$(4) \qquad \psi = \omega^\lambda \rho_0 + \omega^{\lambda-1}\rho_1 + \ldots + \rho_\lambda.$$

If μ and λ are different and, say, $\mu < \lambda$, we have by (2) $\phi + \psi = \psi$, and therefore $\phi < \psi$.

[230] If $\mu = \lambda$, ν_0, and ρ_0 are different, and, say, $\nu_0 < \rho_0$, we have by (2)

$$\phi + \left(\omega^\lambda(\rho_0 - \nu_0) + \omega^{\lambda-1}\rho_1 + \ldots + \rho_\mu\right) = \psi,$$

and therefore

$$\phi < \psi.$$

If, finally,

$$\mu = \lambda, \quad \nu_0 = \rho_0, \; \nu_1 = \rho_1, \; \ldots \nu_{\sigma-1} = \rho_{\sigma-1}, \quad \sigma \overline{\overline{<}} \mu,$$

but ν_σ is different from ρ_σ and, say, $\nu_\sigma < \rho_\sigma$, we have by (2)

$$\phi + \left(\omega^{\lambda-\sigma}(\rho_\sigma - \nu_\sigma) + \omega^{\lambda-\sigma-1}\rho_{\sigma+1} + \ldots + \rho_\mu\right) = \psi,$$

and therefore again

$$\phi < \psi.$$

Thus, we see that only in the case of complete identity of the expressions ϕ and ψ can the numbers represented by them be equal.

The *addition* of ϕ and ψ leads to the following result :

(*a*) If $\mu < \lambda$, then, as we have remarked above,

$$\phi + \psi = \psi;$$

(*b*) If $\mu = \lambda$, then we have

$$\phi + \psi = \omega^\lambda(\nu_0 + \rho_0) + \omega^{\lambda-1}\rho_1 + \ldots + \rho_\lambda;$$

(c) If $\mu > \lambda$, we have

$$\phi + \psi = \omega^\mu \nu_0 + \omega^{\mu-1}\nu_1 + \ldots + \omega^{\lambda+1}\nu_{\mu-\lambda-1} + \omega^\lambda(\nu_{\mu-\lambda} + \rho_0)$$
$$+ \omega^{\lambda-1}\rho_1 + \ldots + \rho_\lambda.$$

In order to carry out the *multiplication* of ϕ and ψ, we remark that, if ρ is a finite number which is different from zero, we have the formula :

$$(5) \qquad \phi\rho = \omega^\mu \nu_0 \rho + \omega^{\mu-1}\nu_1 + \ldots + \nu_\mu.$$

It easily results from the carrying out of the sum consisting of ρ terms $\phi + \phi + \ldots + \phi$. By means of the repeated application of the theorem G of § 15 we get, further, remembering the theorem F of § 15,

$$(6) \qquad\qquad \phi\omega = \omega^{\mu+1},$$

and consequently also

$$(7) \qquad\qquad \phi\omega^\lambda = \omega^{\mu+\lambda}.$$

By the distributive law, numbered (8) of § 14, we have

$$\phi\psi = \phi\omega^\lambda \rho_0 + \phi\omega^{\lambda-1}\rho_1 + \ldots + \phi\omega\rho_{\lambda-1} + \phi\rho_\lambda.$$

Thus the formulæ (4), (5), and (7) give the following result :

(a) If $\rho_\lambda = 0$, we have

$$\phi\psi = \omega^{\mu+\lambda}\rho_0 + \omega^{\mu+\lambda-1}\rho_1 + \ldots + \omega^{\mu+1}\rho_{\lambda-1} = \omega^\mu \psi \, ;$$

(b) If ρ_λ is not equal to zero, we have

$$\phi\psi = \omega^{\mu+\lambda}\rho_0 + \omega^{\mu+\lambda-1}\rho_1 + \ldots + \omega^{\mu+1}\rho_{\lambda-1} + \omega^\mu \nu_0 \rho_\lambda$$
$$+ \omega^{\mu-1}\nu_1 + \ldots + \nu_\mu.$$

[231] We arrive at a remarkable resolution of the numbers ϕ in the following manner. Let

$$(8) \qquad \phi = \omega^\mu \kappa_0 + \omega^{\mu_1} \kappa_1 + \ldots + \omega^{\mu_\tau} \kappa_\tau,$$

where

$$\mu > \mu_1 > \mu_2 > \ldots > \mu_\tau \geqq 0$$

and $\kappa_0, \kappa_1, \ldots, \kappa_\tau$ are finite numbers which are different from zero. Then we have

$$\phi = (\omega^{\mu_1} \kappa_1 + \omega^{\mu_2} \kappa_2 + \ldots + \omega^{\mu_\tau} \kappa_\tau)(\omega^{\mu - \mu_1} \kappa_0 + 1).$$

By the repeated application of this formula we get

$$\phi = \omega^{\mu_\tau} \kappa_\tau (\omega^{\mu_{\tau-1} - \mu_\tau} \kappa_{\tau-1} + 1)(\omega^{\mu_{\tau-2} - \mu_{\tau-1}} \kappa_{\tau-2} + 1) \ldots$$
$$(\omega^{\mu - \mu_1} \kappa_0 + 1).$$

But, now,

$$\omega^\lambda \kappa + 1 = (\omega^\lambda + 1)\kappa,$$

if κ is a finite number which is different from zero; so that :

$$(9) \quad \phi = \omega^{\mu_\tau} \kappa_\tau (\omega^{\mu_{\tau-1} - \mu_\tau} + 1)\kappa_{\tau-1}(\omega^{\mu_{\tau-2} - \mu_{\tau-1}} + 1)\kappa_{\tau-2} \ldots$$
$$\ldots (\omega^{\mu - \mu_1} + 1)\kappa_0.$$

The factors $\omega^\lambda + 1$ which occur here are all irresoluble, and a number ϕ can be represented in this product-form in only one way. If $\mu_\tau = 0$, then ϕ is of the first kind, in all other cases it is of the second kind.

The apparent deviation of the formulæ of this paragraph from those which were given in *Math. Ann.*, vol. xxi, p. 585 (or *Grundlagen*, p. 41), is merely a consequence of the different writing of the product of two numbers : we now put the multiplicand on the left and the multiplicator on the right, but then we put them in the contrary way.

§ 18

The Power * γ^a in the Domain of the Second Number-Class

Let ξ be a variable whose domain consists of the numbers of the first and second number-classes including zero. Let γ and δ be two constants belonging to the same domain, and let

$$\delta > 0, \quad \gamma > 1.$$

We can then assert the following theorem :

A. There is one wholly determined one-valued function $f(\xi)$ of the variable ξ such that :

(*a*) $$f(0) = \delta.$$

(*b*) If ξ' and ξ'' are any two values of ξ, and if

$$\xi' < \xi'',$$

then

$$f(\xi') < f(\xi'').$$

[232] (*c*) For every value of ξ we have

$$f(\xi + 1) = f(\xi)\gamma.$$

(*d*) If $\{\xi_\nu\}$ is any fundamental series, then $\{f(\xi_\nu)\}$ is one also, and if we have

$$\xi = \operatorname{Lim}_\nu \xi_\nu,$$

then

$$f(\xi) = \operatorname{Lim}_\nu f(\xi_\nu).$$

* [Here obviously it is *Potenz* and not *Mächtigkeit*.]

Proof.—By (*a*) and (*c*), we have

$$f(1) = \delta\gamma, \quad f(2) = \delta\gamma\gamma, \quad f(3) = \delta\gamma\gamma\gamma, \quad \dots,$$

and, because $\delta > 0$ and $\gamma > 1$, we have

$$f(1) < f(2) < f(3) < \dots < f(\nu) < f(\nu+1) < \dots$$

Thus the function $f(\xi)$ is wholly determined for the domain $\xi < \omega$. Let us now suppose that the theorem is valid for all values of ξ which are less than α, where α is any number of the second number-class, then it is also valid for $\xi \le \alpha$. For if α is of the first kind, we have from (*c*):

$$f(\alpha) = f(\alpha_{-1})\gamma > f(\alpha_{-1});$$

so that the conditions (*b*), (*c*), and (*d*) are satisfied for $\xi \le \alpha$. But if α is of the second kind and $\{\alpha_\nu\}$ is a fundamental series such that $\operatorname{Lim}_\nu \alpha_\nu = \alpha$, then it follows from (*b*) that also $\{f(\alpha_\nu)\}$ is a fundamental series, and from (*d*) that $f(\alpha) = \operatorname{Lim}_\nu f(\alpha_\nu)$. If we take another fundamental series $\{\alpha'_\nu\}$ such that $\operatorname{Lim}_\nu \alpha'_\nu = \alpha$, then, because of (*b*), the two fundamental series $\{f(\alpha_\nu)\}$ and $\{f(\alpha'_\nu)\}$ are coherent, and thus also $f(\alpha) = \operatorname{Lim}_\nu f(\alpha'_\nu)$. The value of $f(\alpha)$ is, consequently, uniquely determined in this case also.

If α' is any number less than α, we easily convince ourselves that $f(\alpha') < f(\alpha)$. The conditions (*b*), (*c*), and (*d*) are also satisfied for $\xi \lessgtr \alpha$. Hence follows the validity of the theorem *for all values* of ξ. For if there were exceptional values of ξ for which it did not hold, then, by theorem B of § 16, one of

them, which we will call a, would have to be the
least. Then the theorem would be valid for $\xi < a$,
but not for $\xi \leqq a$, and this would be in contradiction
with what we have proved. Thus there is for the
whole domain of ξ one and only one function $f(\xi)$
which satisfies the conditions (a) to (d).

[**233**] If we attribute to the constant δ the value 1
and then denote the function $f(\xi)$ by

$$\gamma^\xi,$$

we can formulate the following theorem :

B. If γ is any constant greater than 1 which
belongs to the first or second number-class, there
is a wholly definite function γ^ξ of ξ such that :

(a) $\gamma^0 = 1$;

(b) If $\xi' < \xi''$ then $\gamma^{\xi'} < \gamma^{\xi''}$;

(c) For every value of ξ we have $\gamma^{\xi+1} = \gamma^\xi \gamma$;

(d) If $\{\xi_\nu\}$ is a fundamental series, then $\{\gamma^{\xi_\nu}\}$
is such a series, and we have, if $\xi = \operatorname*{Lim}_\nu \xi_\nu$, the
equation

$$\gamma^\xi = \operatorname*{Lim}_\nu \gamma^{\xi_\nu}.$$

We can also assert the theorem :

C. If $f(\xi)$ is the function of ξ which is characterized
in theorem A, we have

$$f(\xi) = \delta \gamma^\xi.$$

Proof.—If we pay attention to (24) of § 14,
we easily convince ourselves that the function $\delta \gamma^\xi$
satisfies, not only the conditions (a), (b), and (c)
of theorem A, but also the condition (d) of this

theorem. On account of the uniqueness of the function $f(\xi)$, it must therefore be identical with $\delta\gamma^{\xi}$.

D. If a and β are any two numbers of the first or second number-class, including zero, we have

$$\gamma^{a+\beta} = \gamma^a\gamma^{\beta}.$$

Proof.—We consider the function $\phi(\xi) = \gamma^{a+\xi}$. Paying attention to the fact that, by formula (23) of § 14,

$$\text{Lim} \, (a+\xi_\nu) = a + \text{Lim} \, \xi_\nu,$$
$$\quad \nu \qquad\qquad\qquad \nu$$

we recognize that $\phi(\xi)$ satisfies the following four conditions :

(*a*) $\phi(0) = \gamma^a$;

(*b*) If $\xi' < \xi''$, then $\phi(\xi') < \phi(\xi'')$;

(*c*) For every value of ξ we have $\phi(\xi+1) = \phi(\xi)\gamma$;

(*d*) If $\{\xi_\nu\}$ is a fundamental series such that $\text{Lim} \, \xi_\nu = \xi$, we have
ν

$$\phi(\xi) = \text{Lim} \, \phi(\xi_\nu).$$
$$\qquad\quad \nu$$

By theorem C we have, when we put $\delta = \gamma^a$,

$$\phi(\xi) = \gamma^a\gamma^{\xi}.$$

If we put $\xi = \beta$ in this, we have

$$\gamma^{a+\beta} = \gamma^a\gamma^{\beta}.$$

E. If a and β are any two numbers of the first or second number-class, including zero, we have

$$\gamma^{a\beta} = (\gamma^a)^{\beta}.$$

[234] *Proof.*—Let us consider the function $\psi(\xi) = \gamma^{a\xi}$ and remark that, by (24) of § 14, we

always have $\text{Lim}_{\nu} \, \alpha \xi_{\nu} = \alpha \, \text{Lim}_{\nu} \, \xi_{\nu}$, then we can, by theorem D, assert the following :

(*a*) $\psi(0) = 1$;

(*b*) If $\xi' < \xi''$, then $\psi(\xi') < \psi(\xi'')$;

(*c*) For every value of ξ we have $\psi(\xi + 1) = \psi(\xi)\gamma^{\alpha}$;

(*d*) If $\{\xi_{\nu}\}$ is a fundamental series, then $\{\psi(\xi_{\nu})\}$ is also such a series, and we have, if $\xi = \text{Lim}_{\nu} \, \xi_{\nu}$, the equation $\psi(\xi) = \text{Lim}_{\nu} \, \psi(\xi_{\nu})$.

Thus, by theorem C, if we substitute in it 1 for δ and γ^{α} for γ,

$$\psi(\xi) = (\gamma^{\alpha})^{\xi}.$$

On the *magnitude* of γ^{ξ} in comparison with ξ we can assert the following theorem :

F. If $\gamma > 1$, we have, for every value of ξ,

$$\gamma^{\xi} \geqq \xi.$$

Proof.—In the cases $\xi = 0$ and $\xi = 1$ the theorem is immediately evident. We now show that, if it holds for all values of ξ which are smaller than a given number $\alpha > 1$, it also holds for $\xi = \alpha$.

If α is of the first kind, we have, by supposition,

$$\alpha_{-1} \leqq \gamma^{\alpha - 1},$$

and consequently

$$\alpha_{-1}\gamma \lessgtr \gamma^{\alpha - 1}\gamma = \gamma^{\alpha}.$$

Hence

$$\gamma^{\alpha} \geqq \alpha_{-1} + \alpha_{-1}(\gamma - 1).$$

Since both α_{-1} and $\gamma - 1$ are at least equal to 1, and $\alpha_{-1} + 1 = \alpha$, we have

$$\gamma^{\alpha} \geqq \alpha.$$

If, on the other hand, a is of the second kind and

$$a = \operatorname*{Lim}_{\nu} a_{\nu},$$

then, because $a_{\nu} < a$, we have by supposition

$$a_{\nu} \leqq \gamma^{a_{\nu}}.$$

Consequently

$$\operatorname*{Lim}_{\nu} a_{\nu} \leqq \operatorname*{Lim}_{\nu} \gamma^{a_{\nu}},$$

that is to say,

$$a \leqq \gamma^{a}.$$

If, now, there were values of ξ for which

$$\xi > \gamma^{\xi},$$

one of them, by theorem B of § 16, would have to be the least. If this number is denoted by a, we would have, for $\xi < a$,

[235] $$\xi \leqq \gamma^{\xi};$$

but

$$a > \gamma^{a},$$

which contradicts what we have proved above. Thus we have for all values of ξ

$$\gamma^{\xi} \geqq \xi.$$

§ 19

The Normal Form of the Numbers of the Second Number-Class

Let a be any number of the second number-class. The power ω^{ξ} will be, for sufficiently great values of ξ, greater than a. By theorem F of § 18, this is always the case for $\xi > a$; but in general it will also happen for smaller values of ξ.

By theorem B of § 16, there must be, among the values of ξ for which

$$\omega^{\xi} > a,$$

one which is the least. We will denote it by β, and we easily convince ourselves that it cannot be a number of the second kind. If, indeed, we had

$$\beta = \underset{\nu}{\text{Lim}} \ \beta_{\nu},$$

we would have, since $\beta_{\nu} < \beta$,

$$\omega^{\beta_{\nu}} \lneqq a,$$

and consequently

$$\underset{\nu}{\text{Lim}} \ \omega^{\beta_{\nu}} \lneqq a.$$

Thus we would have

$$\omega^{\beta} \lneqq a,$$

whereas we have

$$\omega^{\beta} > a.$$

Therefore β is of the first kind. We denote β_{-1} by a_0, so that $\beta = a_0 + 1$, and consequently can assert that there is a wholly determined number a_0 of the first or second number-class which satisfies the two conditions :

$$(1) \qquad \omega^{a_0} \leqq a, \quad \omega^{a_0}\omega > a.$$

From the second condition we conclude that

$$\omega^{a_0}\nu \leqq a$$

does not hold for all finite values of ν, for if it did we would have

$$\operatorname*{Lim}_{\nu} \omega^{a_0}\nu = \omega^{a_0}\omega \leqq a.$$

The least finite number ν for which

$$\omega^{a_0}\nu > a$$

will be denoted by $\kappa_0 + 1$. Because of (1), we have $\kappa_0 > 0$.

[236] There is, therefore, a wholly determined number κ_0 of the first number-class such that

$$(2) \qquad \omega^{a_0}\kappa_0 \leqq a, \qquad \omega^{a_0}(\kappa_0 + 1) > a.$$

If we put $a - \omega^{a_0}\kappa_0 = a'$, we have

$$(3) \qquad\qquad a = \omega^{a_0}\kappa_0 + a'$$

and

$$(4) \qquad\qquad 0 \leqq a' < \omega^{a_0}, \quad 0 < \kappa_0 < \omega.$$

But a can be represented in the form (3) under the conditions (4) in only a single way. For from (3) and (4) follow inversely the conditions (2) and thence the conditions (1). But only the number $a_0 = \beta_{-1}$ satisfies the conditions (1), and by the conditions (2) the finite number κ_0 is uniquely determined. From (1) and (4) follows, by paying attention to theorem F of § 18, that

$$a' < a, \quad a_0 \leqq a.$$

Thus we can assert the following theorem :

A. Every number a of the second number-class

can be brought, and brought in only one way, into the form

$$a = \omega^{a_0}\kappa_0 + a',$$

where

$$0 \leqq a' < \omega^{a_0}, \quad 0 < \kappa_0 < \omega,$$

and a' is always smaller than a, but a_0 is smaller than or equal to a.

If a' is a number of the second number-class, we can apply theorem A to it, and we have

$$(5) \qquad a' = \omega^{a_1}\kappa_1 + a'',$$

where

$$0 \leqq a'' < \omega^{a_1}, \quad 0 < \kappa_1 < \omega,$$

and

$$a_1 < a_0, \quad a'' < a'.$$

In general we get a further sequence of analogous equations :

$$(6) \qquad a'' = \omega^{a_2}\kappa_2 + a''',$$

$$(7) \qquad a''' = \omega^{a_3}\kappa_3 + a^{\mathrm{iv}}.$$

$$\cdot \quad \cdot \quad \cdot \quad \cdot \quad \cdot \quad \cdot$$

But this sequence cannot be infinite, but must necessarily break off.   For the numbers a, a', a'', . . . decrease in magnitude :

$$a > a' > a'' > a''' \ldots$$

If a series of decreasing transfinite numbers were infinite, then no term would be the least ; and this is impossible by theorem B of § 16.   Consequently we must have, for a certain finite numerical value τ,

$$a^{(\tau+1)} = 0.$$

[237] If we now connect the equations (3), (5), (6), and (7) with one another, we get the theorem :

B. Every number a of the second number-class can be represented, and represented in only one way, in the form

$$a = \omega^{a_0}\kappa_0 + \omega^{a_1}\kappa_1 + \ldots + \omega^{a_\tau}\kappa_\tau,$$

where $a_0, a_1, \ldots a_\tau$ are numbers of the first or second number-class, such that :

$$a_0 > a_1 > a_2 > \ldots > a_\tau \geqq 0,$$

while $\kappa_0, \kappa_1, \ldots \kappa_\tau, \tau + 1$ are numbers of the first number-class which are different from zero.

The form of numbers of the second number-class which is here shown will be called their "normal form"; a_0 is called the "degree" and a_τ the "exponent" of a. For $\tau = 0$, degree and exponent are equal to one another.

According as the exponent a_τ is equal to or greater than zero, a is a number of the first or second kind.

Let us take another number β in the normal form :

$$(8) \qquad \beta = \omega^{\beta_0}\lambda_0 + \omega^{\beta_1}\lambda_1 + \ldots + \omega^{\beta_\sigma}\lambda_\sigma.$$

The formulæ :

$$(9) \qquad \omega^{a'}\kappa' + \omega^{a'}\kappa = \omega^{a'}(\kappa' + \kappa),$$

$$(10) \qquad \omega^{a'}\kappa' + \omega^{a''}\kappa'' = \omega^{a''}\kappa'', \quad a' < a'',$$

where $\kappa, \kappa', \kappa''$ here denote finite numbers, serve both for the comparison of a with β and for the carrying out of their sum and difference. These are generalizations of the formulæ (2) and (3) of § 17.

For the formation of the product $\alpha\beta$, the following formulæ come into consideration :

(11) $\alpha\lambda = \omega^{\alpha_0}\kappa_0\lambda + \omega^{\alpha_1}\kappa_1 + \ldots + \omega^{\alpha_\tau}\kappa_\tau, \quad 0 < \lambda < \omega ;$

(12) $\alpha\omega = \omega^{\alpha_0+1} ;$

(13) $\alpha\omega^{\beta'} = \omega^{\alpha_0+\beta'}, \quad \beta' > 0.$

The exponentiation α^β can be easily carried out on the basis of the following formulæ :

(14) $\alpha^\lambda = \omega^{\alpha_0\lambda}\kappa_0 + \ldots, \quad 0 < \lambda < \omega.$

The terms not written on the right have a lower degree than the first. Hence follows readily that the fundamental series $\{\alpha^\lambda\}$ and $\{\omega^{\alpha_0\lambda}\}$ are coherent, so that

(15) $\alpha^\omega = \omega^{\alpha_0\omega}, \quad \alpha_0 > 0.$

Thus, in consequence of theorem E of § 18, we have :

(16) $\alpha^{\omega\beta'} = \omega^{\alpha_0\omega^{\beta'}}, \quad \alpha_0 > 0, \quad \beta' > 0.$

By the help of these formulæ we can prove the following theorems :

[238] C. If the first terms $\omega^{\alpha_0}\kappa_0$, $\omega^{\beta_0}\lambda_0$ of the normal forms of the two numbers α and β are not equal, then α is less or greater than β according as $\omega^{\alpha_0}\kappa_0$ is less or greater than $\omega^{\beta_0}\lambda_0$. But if we have

$$\omega^{\alpha_0}\kappa_0 = \omega^{\beta_0}\lambda_0, \; \omega^{\alpha_1}\kappa_1 = \omega^{\beta_1}\lambda_1, \ldots, \; \omega^{\alpha_\rho}\kappa_\rho = \omega^{\beta_\rho}\lambda_\rho,$$

and if $\omega^{\alpha_{\rho+1}}\kappa_{\rho+1}$ is less or greater than $\omega^{\beta_{\rho+1}}\lambda_{\rho+1}$, then α is correspondingly less or greater than β.

D. If the degree a_0 of a is less than the degree β_0 of β, we have

$$a + \beta = \beta.$$

If $a_0 = \beta_0$, then

$$a + \beta = \omega^{\beta_0}(\kappa_0 + \lambda_0) + \omega^{\beta_1}\lambda_1 + \ldots + \omega^{\beta_\sigma}\lambda_\sigma.$$

But if

$$a_0 > \beta_0,\ a_1 > \beta_0,\ \ldots,\ a_\rho \geqq \beta_0,\ a_{\rho+1} < \beta_0,$$

then

$$a + \beta = \omega^{a_0}\kappa_0 + \ldots + \omega^{a_\rho}\kappa_\rho + \omega^{\beta_0}\lambda_0 + \omega^{\beta_1}\lambda_1 + \ldots + \omega^{\beta_\sigma}\lambda_\sigma.$$

E. If β is of the second kind ($\beta_\sigma > 0$), then

$$a\beta = \omega^{a_0+\beta_0}\lambda_0 + \omega^{a_0+\beta_1}\lambda_1 + \ldots + \omega^{a_0+\beta_\sigma}\lambda_\sigma = \omega^{a_0}\beta\ ;$$

But if β is of the first kind ($\beta_\sigma = 0$), then

$$a\beta = \omega^{a_0+\beta_0}\lambda_0 + \omega^{a_0+\beta_1}\lambda_1 + \ldots + \omega^{a_0+\beta_\sigma-1}\lambda_{\sigma-1} + \omega^{a_0}\kappa_0\lambda_\sigma$$
$$+ \omega^{a_1}\kappa_1 + \ldots + \omega^{a_\tau}\kappa_\tau.$$

F. If β is of the second kind ($\beta_\sigma > 0$), then

$$a^\beta = \omega^{a_0\beta}.$$

But if β is of the first kind ($\beta_\sigma = 0$), and indeed $\beta = \beta' + \lambda_\sigma$, where β' is of the second kind, we have:

$$a^\beta = \omega^{a_0\beta'}a^{\lambda_\sigma}.$$

G. Every number a of the second number-class can be represented, in only one way, in the product-form :

$$a = \omega^{\gamma_0}\kappa_\tau(\omega^{\gamma_1} + 1)\kappa_{\tau-1}(\omega^{\gamma_2} + 1)\kappa_{\tau-2} \ldots (\omega^{\gamma_\tau} + 1)\kappa_0,$$

and we have

$$\gamma_0 = a_\tau,\ \gamma_1 = a_{\tau-1} - a_\tau,\ \gamma_2 = a_{\tau-2} - a_{\tau-1},\ \ldots,\ \gamma_\tau = a_0 - a_1,$$

whilst κ_0, κ_1, . . . κ_τ have the same denotation as in the normal form. The factors $\omega^\gamma + 1$ are all irresoluble.

H. Every number a of the second kind which belongs to the second number-class can be represented, and represented in only one way, in the form

$$a = \omega^{\gamma_0} a',$$

where $\gamma_0 > 0$ and a' is a number of the first kind which belongs to the first or second number-class.

[239] I. In order that two numbers a and β of the second number-class should satisfy the relation

$$a + \beta = \beta + a,$$

it is necessary and sufficient that they should have the form

$$a = \gamma\mu, \quad \beta = \gamma\nu,$$

where μ and ν are numbers of the first number-class.

K. In order that two numbers a and β of the second number-class, which are both of the first kind, should satisfy the relation

$$a\beta = \beta a,$$

it is necessary and sufficient that they should have the form

$$a = \gamma^\mu, \quad \beta = \gamma^\nu,$$

where μ and ν are numbers of the first number-class.

In order to exemplify the extent of the *normal form* dealt with and the *product-form* immediately connected with it, of the numbers of the second number-class, the proofs, which are founded on them, of the two last theorems, I and K, may here follow.

From the supposition

$$a + \beta = \beta + a$$

we first conclude that the degree a_0 of a must be equal to the degree β_0 of β. For if, say, $a_0 < \beta_0$, we would have, by theorem D,

$$a + \beta = \beta,$$

and consequently

$$\beta + a = \beta,$$

which is not possible, since, by (2) of § 14,

$$\beta + a > \beta.$$

Thus we may put

$$a = \omega^{a_0}\mu + a', \quad \beta = \omega^{a_0}\nu + \beta',$$

where the degrees of the numbers a' and β' are less than a_0, and μ and ν are infinite numbers which are different from zero. Now, by theorem D we have

$$a + \beta = \omega^{a_0}(\mu + \nu) + \beta', \quad \beta + a = \omega^{a_0}(\mu + \nu) + a',$$

and consequently

$$\omega^{a_0}(\mu + \nu) + \beta' = \omega^{a_0}(\mu + \nu) + a'.$$

By theorem D of § 14 we have consequently

$$\beta' = a'.$$

Thus we have

$$a = \omega^{a_0}\mu + a', \quad \beta = \omega^{a_0}\nu + a',$$

[240] and if we put

$$\omega^{a_0} + a' = \gamma$$

we have, by (11) :

$$a = \gamma\mu, \quad \beta = \gamma\nu.$$

Let us suppose, on the other hand, that a and β are two numbers which belong to the second number-class, are of the first kind, and satisfy the condition

$$a\beta = \beta a,$$

and we suppose that

$$a > \beta.$$

We will imagine both numbers, by theorem G, in their product-form, and let

$$a = \delta a', \quad \beta = \delta\beta',$$

where a' and β' are without a common factor (besides 1) at the left end. We have then

$$a' > \beta',$$

and

$$a'\delta\beta' = \beta'\delta a'.$$

All the numbers which occur here and farther on are of the first kind, because this was supposed of a and β.

The last equation, when we refer to theorem G, shows that a' and β' cannot be both transfinite, because, in this case, there would be a common factor at the left end. Neither can they be both finite ; for then δ would be transfinite, and, if κ is the finite factor at the left end of δ, we would have

$$a'\kappa = \beta'\kappa,$$

and thus

$$\alpha' = \beta'.$$

Thus there remains only the possibility that

$$\alpha' > \omega, \quad \beta' < \omega.$$

But the finite number β' must be 1 :

$$\beta' = 1,$$

because otherwise it would be contained as part in the finite factor at the left end of α'.

We arrive at the result that $\beta = \delta$, consequently

$$\alpha = \beta\alpha',$$

where α' is a number belonging to the second number-class, which is of the first kind, and must be less than α :

$$\alpha' < \alpha.$$

Between α' and β the relation

$$\alpha'\beta = \beta\alpha'$$

subsists.

[241] Consequently if also $\alpha' > \beta$, we conclude in the same way the existence of a transfinite number of the first kind α'' which is less than α' and such that

$$\alpha' = \beta\alpha'', \quad \alpha''\beta = \beta\alpha''.$$

If also α'' is greater than β, there is such a number α''' less than α'', such that

$$\alpha'' = \beta\alpha''', \quad \alpha'''\beta = \beta\alpha''',$$

and so on. The series of decreasing numbers, α, α', α'', α''', . . ., must, by theorem B of § 16, break off.   Thus, for a definite finite index ρ_0, we must have

$$a^{(\rho_0)} \leqq \beta.$$

If

$$a^{(\rho_0)} = \beta,$$

we have

$$a = \beta^{\rho_0+1}, \quad \beta = \beta\;;$$

the theorem K would then be proved, and we would have

$$\gamma = \beta, \quad \mu = \rho_0 + 1, \quad \nu = 1.$$

But if

$$a^{(\rho_0)} < \beta,$$

then we put

$$a^{(\rho_0)} = \beta_1,$$

and have

$$a = \beta^{\rho_0}\beta_1, \quad \beta\beta_1 = \beta_1\beta, \quad \beta_1 < \beta.$$

Thus there is also a finite number ρ_1 such that

$$\beta = \beta_1{}^{\rho_1}\beta_2, \quad \beta_1\beta_2 = \beta_2\beta_1, \quad \beta_2 < \beta_1.$$

In general, we have analogously :

$$\beta_1 = \beta_2{}^{\rho_2}\beta_3, \quad \beta_2\beta_3 = \beta_3\beta_2, \quad \beta_3 < \beta_2,$$

and so on.   The series of decreasing numbers β_1, β_2, β_3, . . . also must, by theorem B of § 16, break off.   Thus there exists a finite number κ such that

$$\beta_{\kappa-1} = \beta_\kappa{}^{\rho_\kappa}.$$

If we put

$$\beta_\kappa = \gamma,$$

then

$$a = \gamma^\mu, \quad \beta = \gamma^\nu,$$

where μ and ν are numerator and denominator of the continued fraction.

$$\frac{\mu}{\nu} = \rho_0 + \frac{1}{\rho_1 +} \cdot \quad \cdot \quad \cdot + \frac{1}{\rho_\kappa} \cdot$$

[242] § 20

The ϵ-Numbers of the Second Number-Class

The degree a_0 of a number a is, as is immediately evident from the normal form :

(1) $\quad a = \omega^{a_0}\kappa_0 + \omega^{a_1}\kappa_1 + \ldots, \quad a_0 > a_1 > \ldots, \quad 0 < \kappa_\nu < \omega,$

when we pay attention to theorem F of § 18, never greater than a ; but it is a question whether there are not numbers for which $a_0 = a$. In such a case the normal form of a would reduce to the first term, and this term would be equal to ω^a, that is to say, a would be a root of the equation

(2) $\qquad \omega^\xi = \xi.$

On the other hand, every root a of this equation would have the normal form ω^a ; its degree would be equal to itself.

The numbers of the second number-class which are· equal to their degree coincide, therefore, with the roots of the equation (2). It is our problem to determine these roots in their totality. To distinguish them from all other numbers we will call them the "ϵ-numbers of the second number-class."

That there *are* such ϵ-numbers results from the following theorem :

A. If γ is any number of the first or second number-class which does not satisfy the equation (2), it determines a fundamental series $\{\gamma\}$ by means of the equations

$$\gamma_1 = \omega^\gamma, \quad \gamma_2 = \omega^{\gamma_1}, \quad \ldots, \quad \gamma_\nu = \omega^{\gamma_{\nu-1}}, \quad \ldots$$

The limit $\underset{\nu}{\text{Lim}}\ \gamma_\nu = E(\gamma)$ of this fundamental series is always an ϵ-number.

Proof.—Since γ is not an ϵ-number, we have $\omega^\gamma > \gamma$, that is to say, $\gamma_1 > \gamma$. Thus, by theorem B of § 18, we have also $\omega^{\gamma_1} > \omega^\gamma$, that is to say, $\gamma_2 > \gamma_1$; and in the same way follows that $\gamma_3 > \gamma_2$, and so on. The series $\{\gamma_\nu\}$ is thus a fundamental series. We denote its limit, which is a function of γ, by $E(\gamma)$ and have :

$$\omega^{E(\gamma)} = \underset{\nu}{\text{Lim}}\ \omega^\gamma = \underset{\nu}{\text{Lim}}\ \gamma_{\nu+1} = E(\gamma).$$

Consequently $E(\gamma)$ is an ϵ-number.

B. The number $\epsilon_0 = E(1) = \underset{\nu}{\text{Lim}}\ \omega_\nu$, where

$$\omega_1 = \omega, \quad \omega_2 = \omega^{\omega_1}, \quad \omega_3 = \omega^{\omega_2}, \quad \ldots, \quad \omega_\nu = \omega^{\omega_{\nu-1}}, \quad \ldots,$$

is the least of all the ϵ-numbers.

[243] *Proof.*—Let ϵ' be any ϵ-number, so that

$$\omega^{\epsilon'} = \epsilon'.$$

Since $\epsilon' > \omega$, we have $\omega^{\epsilon'} > \omega^\omega$, that is to say, $\epsilon' > \omega_1$. Similarly $\omega^{\epsilon'} > \omega^{\omega_1}$, that is to say, $\epsilon' > \omega_2$, and so on. We have in general

$$\epsilon' > \omega_\nu,$$

and consequently

$$\epsilon' \geqq \underset{\nu}{\text{Lim}}\ \omega_\nu,$$

that is to say,

$$\epsilon' \geqq \epsilon_0.$$

Thus $\epsilon_0 = \mathrm{E}(1)$ is the least of all ϵ-numbers.

C. If ϵ' is any ϵ-number, ϵ'' is the next greater ϵ-number, and γ is any number which lies between them :

$$\epsilon' < \gamma < \epsilon'',$$

then $\mathrm{E}(\gamma) = \epsilon''$.

Proof.—From

$$\epsilon' < \gamma < \epsilon''$$

follows

$$\omega^{\epsilon'} < \omega^\gamma < \omega^{\epsilon''},$$

that is to say,

$$\epsilon' < \gamma_1 < \epsilon''.$$

Similarly we conclude

$$\epsilon' < \gamma_2 < \epsilon'',$$

and so on.   We have, in general,

$$\epsilon' < \gamma_\nu < \epsilon'',$$

and thus

$$\epsilon' < \mathrm{E}(\gamma) \leqq \epsilon''.$$

By theorem A, $\mathrm{E}(\gamma)$ is an ϵ-number.   Since ϵ'' is the ϵ-number which follows ϵ' next in order of magnitude, $\mathrm{E}(\gamma)$ cannot be less than ϵ'', and thus we must have

$$\mathrm{E}(\gamma) = \epsilon''.$$

Since $\epsilon' + 1$ is not an ϵ-number, simply because all ϵ-numbers, as follows from the equation of definition

$\xi = \omega^\xi$, are of the second kind, $\epsilon' + 1$ is certainly less than ϵ'', and thus we have the following theorem :

D. If ϵ' is any ϵ-number, then $E(\epsilon' + 1)$ is the next greater ϵ-number.

To the least ϵ-number, ϵ_0, follows, then, the next greater one:

$$\epsilon_1 = E(\epsilon_0 + 1),$$

[244] to this the next greater number :

$$\epsilon_2 = E(\epsilon_1 + 1),$$

and so on. Quite generally, we have for the $(\nu + 1)$th ϵ-number in order of magnitude the formula of recursion

$$(3) \qquad \epsilon_\nu = E(\epsilon_{\nu-1} + 1).$$

But that the infinite series

$$\epsilon_0, \; \epsilon_1, \; \ldots \epsilon_\nu, \; \ldots$$

by no means embraces the totality of ϵ-numbers results from the following theorem :

E. If ϵ, ϵ', ϵ'', $\ldots$ is any infinite series of ϵ-numbers such that

$$\epsilon < \epsilon' < \epsilon'' \ldots \epsilon^{(\nu)} < \epsilon^{(\nu+1)} < \ldots,$$

then $\operatorname{Lim}_\nu \epsilon^{(\nu)}$ is an ϵ-number, and, in fact, the ϵ-number which follows next in order of magnitude to all the numbers $\epsilon^{(\nu)}$.

Proof.—

$$\omega^{\operatorname{Lim}_\nu \epsilon^{(\nu)}} = \operatorname{Lim}_\nu \omega^{\epsilon^{(\nu)}} = \operatorname{Lim}_\nu \epsilon^{(\nu)}.$$

That Lim $\epsilon^{(\nu)}$ is the ϵ-number which follows next in order of magnitude to all the numbers $\epsilon^{(\nu)}$ results from the fact that Lim $\epsilon^{(\nu)}$ is the number of the second number-class which follows next in order of magnitude to all the numbers $\epsilon^{(\nu)}$.

F. The totality of ϵ-numbers of the second number-class forms, when arranged in order of magnitude, a well-ordered aggregate of the type Ω of the second number-class in its order of magnitude, and has thus the power Aleph-one.

Proof.—The totality of ϵ-numbers of the second number-class, when arranged in their order of magnitude, forms, by theorem C of § 16, a well-ordered aggregate :

(4) $\quad \epsilon_0, \epsilon_1, \ldots, \epsilon_\nu, \ldots \epsilon_{\omega+1}, \ldots \epsilon_{\alpha'} \ldots,$

whose law of formation is expressed in the theorems D and E. Now, if the index α' did not successively take all the numerical values of the second number-class, there would be a least number α which it did not reach. But this would contradict the theorem D, if α were of the first kind, and theorem E, if α were of the second kind. Thus α' takes all numerical values of the second number-class.

If we denote the type of the second number-class by Ω, the type of (4) is

$$\omega + \Omega = \omega + \omega^2 + (\Omega - \omega^2).$$

[245] But since $\omega + \omega^2 = \omega^2$, we have

$$\omega + \Omega = \Omega;$$

and consequently

$$\overline{\omega + \Omega} = \overline{\Omega} = \aleph_1.$$

G. If ϵ is any ϵ-number and α is any number of the first or second number-class which is less than ϵ :

$$\alpha < \epsilon,$$

then ϵ satisfies the three equations :

$$\alpha + \epsilon = \epsilon, \quad \alpha\epsilon = \epsilon, \quad \alpha^\epsilon = \epsilon.$$

Proof.—If α_0 is the degree of α, we have $\alpha_0 \leq \alpha$, and consequently, because of $\alpha < \epsilon$, we also have $\alpha_0 < \epsilon$. But the degree of $\epsilon = \omega^\epsilon$ is ϵ ; thus α has a less degree than ϵ. Consequently, by theorem D of § 19,

$$\alpha + \epsilon = \epsilon,$$

and thus

$$\alpha_0 + \epsilon = \epsilon.$$

On the other hand, we have, by formula (13) of § 19,

$$\alpha\epsilon = \alpha\omega^\epsilon = \omega^{\alpha_0 + \epsilon} = \omega^\epsilon = \epsilon,$$

and thus

$$\alpha_0 \epsilon = \epsilon.$$

Finally, paying attention to the formula (16) of § 19,

$$\alpha^\epsilon = \alpha\omega^\epsilon = \omega^{\alpha_0}\omega^\epsilon = \omega^{\alpha_0 \epsilon} = \omega^\epsilon = \epsilon.$$

H. If α is any number of the second number-class, the equation

$$\alpha^\xi = \xi$$

has no other roots than the ϵ-numbers which are greater than α.

Proof.—Let β be a root of the equation

$$\alpha^\xi = \xi,$$

so that

$$\alpha^\beta = \beta.$$

Then, in the first place, from this formula follows that

$$\beta > \alpha.$$

On the other hand, β must be of the second kind, since, if not, we would have

$$\alpha^\beta > \beta.$$

Thus we have, by theorem F of § 19,

$$\alpha^\beta = {}^{\alpha_0\beta}.$$

and consequently

$$\omega^{\alpha_0\beta} = \beta.$$

[246] By theorem F of § 19, we have

$$\omega^{\alpha_0\beta} \geqq \alpha_0\beta,$$

and thus

$$\beta \geqq \alpha_0\beta.$$

But β cannot be greater than $\alpha_0\beta$; consequently

$$\alpha_0\beta = \beta,$$

and thus

$$\omega^\beta = \beta.$$

Therefore β is an ϵ-number which is greater than α.

HALLE, *March* 1897.

NOTES

In a sense the most fundamental advance made in the theoretical arithmetic of finite and transfinite numbers is the purely logical definition of the number-concept. Whereas Cantor (see pp. 74, 86, 112 above) defined "cardinal number" and "ordinal type" as general concepts which arise by means of our mental activity, that is to say, as psychological entities, Gottlob Frege had, in his *Grundlagen der Arithmetik* of 1884, defined the "number (*Anzahl*) of a class *u*" as the class of all those classes which are equivalent (in the sense of pp. 75, 86 above) to *u*. Frege remarked that his "numbers" are the same as what Cantor (see pp. 40, 74, 86 above) had called "powers," and that there was no reason for restricting "numbers" to be finite. Although Frege worked out, in the first volume (1893) of his *Grundgesetze der Arithmetik*, an important part of arithmetic, with a logical accuracy previously unknown and for years afterwards almost unknown, his ideas did not become at all widely known until Bertrand Russell, who had arrived independently at this logical definition of "cardinal number," gave prominence to them in his

Principles of Mathematics of 1903.* The two chief
reasons in favour of this definition are that it
avoids, by a construction of "numbers" out of the
fundamental entities of logic, the assumption that
there are certain new and undefined entities called
"numbers"; and that it allows us to deduce at
once that the class defined is not empty, so that
the cardinal number of *u* "exists" in the sense
defined in logic : in fact, since *u* is equivalent to
itself, the cardinal number of *u* has *u* at least as a
member. Russell also gave an analogous definition
for ordinal types or the more general "relation
numbers."†

An account of much that has been done in the
theory of aggregates since 1897 may be gathered
from A. Schoenflies's reports : *Die Entwickelung
der Lehre von den Punktmannigfaltigkeiten*, Leipzig,
1900 ; part ii, Leipzig, 1908. A second edition
of the first part was published at Leipzig and Berlin
in 1913, in collaboration with H. Hahn, under the
title : *Entwickelung der Mengenlehre und ihrer
Anwendungen*. These three books will be cited
by their respective dates of publication, and, when
references to relevant contributions not mentioned
in these reports are made, full references to the
original place of publication will be given.

---

* Pp. 519, 111–116. *Cf.* Whitehead, *Amer. Journ. of Math.*, vol.
xxiv, 1902, p. 378. For a more modern form of the doctrine, see
Whitehead and Russell, *Principia Mathematica*, vol. ii, Cambridge,
1912, pp. 4, 13.
† *Principles*, pp. 262, 321 ; and *Principia*, vol. ii, pp. 330,
473–510.

Leaving aside the applications of the theory of transfinite numbers to geometry and the theory of functions, the most important advances since 1897 are as follows :

(1) The proof given independently by Ernst Schröder (1896) and Felix Bernstein (1898) of the theorem B on p. 91 above, without the supposition that one of the three relations of magnitude must hold between any two cardinal numbers (1900, pp. 16–18 ; 1913, pp. 34–41 ; 1908, pp. 10–12).

(2) The giving of exactly expressed definitions of arithmetical operations with cardinal numbers and of proofs of the laws of arithmetic for them by A. N. Whitehead (*Amer. Journ. of Math.*, vol. xxiv, 1902, pp. 367–394). *Cf.* Russell, *Principles*, pp. 117–120. A more modern form is given in Whitehead and Russell's *Principia*, vol. ii, pp. 66–186.

(3) Investigations on the question as to whether any aggregate can be brought into the form of a well-ordered aggregate. This question Cantor (*cf.* 1900, p. 49 ; 1913, p. 170 ; and p. 63 above) believed could be answered in the affirmative. The postulate lying at the bottom of this theorem was brought forward in the most definite manner by E. Zermelo and E. Schmidt in 1904, and Zermelo afterwards gave this postulate the form of an "axiom of selection" (1913, pp. 16, 170–184 ; 1908, pp. 33-36). Whitehead and Russell have dealt with great precision with the subject in their *Principia*, vol. i, Cambridge, 1910, pp. 500–568.

It may be remarked that Cantor, in his proof of theorem A on p. 105 above, and in that of theorem C on pp. 161–162 above,* unconsciously used this axiom of infinite selection. Also G. H. Hardy in 1903 (1908, pp. 22–23) used this axiom, unconsciously at first, in a proof that it is possible to have an aggregate of cardinal number $\aleph_1$ in the continuum of real numbers.

But there is another and wholly different question which crops up in attempts at a proof that any aggregate can be well ordered. Cesare Burali-Forti had in 1897 pointed out that the series of all ordinal numbers, which is easily seen to be well ordered, must have the greatest of all ordinal numbers as its type. Yet the type of the above series of ordinal numbers followed by its type must be a greater ordinal number, for $\beta + 1$ is greater than β. Burali-Forti concluded that we must deny Cantor's fundamental theorem in his memoir of 1897. A different use of an argument analogous to Burali-Forti's was made by Philip E. B. Jourdain in a paper written in 1903 and published in 1904 (*Philosophical Magazine*, 6th series, vol. vii, pp. 61–75). The chief interest of this paper is that it contains a proof which is independent of, but practically identical with, that discovered by Cantor in 1895, and of which some

---

* Indeed, we have here to prove that *any* enumerable aggregate of *any* enumerable aggregates gives an enumerable aggregate of the elements last referred to. To prove that $\aleph_0 \cdot \aleph_0 = \aleph_0$, it is not enough to prove the above theorem for *particular* aggregates. And in the general case we have to pick one element out of each of an infinity of classes, no element in each class being distinguished from the others.

trace is preserved in the passage on p. 109 above and in the remark on the theorem A of p. 90. This proof of Cantor's and Jourdain's consists of two parts. In the first part it is established that every cardinal number is either an Aleph or is greater than all Alephs. This part requires the use of Zermelo's axiom ; and Jourdain took the "proof" of this part of the theorem directly from Hardy's paper of 1903 referred to above. Cantor *assumed* the result required, and indeed the result seems very plausible.

The second part of the theorem consists in the proof that the supposition that a cardinal number is greater than all Alephs is impossible. By a slight modification of Burali-Forti's argument, in which modification it is proved that there cannot be a greatest Aleph, the conclusion seems to follow that no cardinal number can be other than an Aleph.

The contradiction discovered by Burali-Forti is the best known to mathematicians ; but the simplest contradiction was discovered * by Russell (*Principles,* pp. 364-368, 101-107) from an application to "the cardinal number of all things" of Cantor's argument of 1892 referred to on pp. 99-100 above. Russell's contradiction can be reduced to the following : If w is the class of all those terms x such that x is not a member of x, then, if w is a member of w, it is plain that w is not a member of w ; while if w is not a member of w, it is equally plain that w is a member of w. The treatment and final solution of

* This argument was discovered in 1900 (see *Monist*, Jan. 1912).

these paradoxes, which concern the foundations of logic and which are closely allied to the logical puzzle known as "the Epimenides,"* has been attempted unsuccessfully by very many mathematicians,† and successfully by Russell (*cf. Principles*, pp. 523–528 ; *Principia*, vol. i, pp. 26–31, 39–90).

The theorem A on p. 105 is required (see theorem D on p. 108) in the proof that the two definitions of infinity coincide. On this point, *cf. Principles*, pp. 121–123 ; *Principia*, vol. i, pp. 569–666 ; vol. ii, pp. 187–298.

(4) Investigation of number-classes in general, and the arithmetic of Alephs by Jourdain in 1904 and 1908, and G. Hessenberg in 1906‡ (1913, pp. 131–136 ; 1908, pp. 13–14).

(5) The definition, by Felix Hausdorff in 1904–1907, of the product of an infinity of ordinal types and hence of exponentiation by a type. This definition is analogous to Cantor's definition of exponentiation for cardinal numbers on p. 95 above.§ *Cf.* 1913, pp. 75–80 ; 1908, pp. 42–45.

(6) Theorems due to J. König (1904) on the

---

* Epimenides was a Cretan who said that all Cretans were liars. Obviously if his statement were true he was a liar. The remark of a man who says, " I am lying," is even more analogous to Russell's w.

† Thus Schoenflies, in his Reports of 1908 and 1913, devotes an undue amount of space to his " solution " of the paradoxes here referred to. This " solution " really consists in saying that these paradoxes do not belong to mathematics but to " philosophy." It may be remarked that Schoenflies seems never to have grasped the meaning and extent of Zermelo's axiom, which Russell has called the " multiplicative axiom."

‡ Just as in the proof that the multiplication of $\aleph_0$ by itself gives $\aleph_0$, the more general theorem here considered involves the multiplicative axiom.

§ *Cf.* Jourdain, *Mess. of Math.* (2), vol. xxxvi, May 1906, pp. 13–16.

inequality of certain cardinal numbers; and the independent generalization of these theorems, together with one of Cantor's (see pp. 81-82 above), by Zermelo and Jourdain in 1908 (1908, pp. 16-17; 1913, pp. 65-67).

(7) Hausdorff's contributions from 1906 to 1908 to the theory of linear ordered aggregates (1913, pp. 185-205; 1908, pp. 40-71).

(8) The investigation of the ordinal types of multiply ordered infinite aggregates by F. Riess in 1903, and Brouwer in 1913 (1913, pp. 85-87).

INDEX

Abel, Niels Henrike, 10.
Abelian functions, 10, 11.
Absolute infinity, 62, 63.
Actuality of numbers, 67.
Addition of cardinal numbers, 80,
    91 ff.
  of ordinal types, 81, 119 ff.
  of transfinite numbers, 63, 66,
    153 ff., 175 ff., 206.
Adherences, 73.
Aggregate, definition of, 46, 47,
    54, 74, 85.
  of bindings, 92.
  of union, 50, 91.
Alembert, Jean Lerond d', 4.
Algebraic numbers, 38 ff., 127.
Aquinas, Thomas, 70.
Aristotle, 55, 70.
Arithmetic, foundations of, with
    Weierstrass, 12.
  with Frege and Russell, 202,
    203.
Arzelà, 73.
Associative law with transfinite
    numbers, 92, 93, 119, 121,
    154, 155.

Baire, René, 73.
Bendixson, Ivar, 73.
Berkeley, George, 55.
Bernoulli, Daniel, 4.
Bernstein, Felix, 204.
Bois-Reymond, Paul du, 22, 34, 51.
Bolzano, Bernard, 13, 14, 17, 21,
    22, 41, 55, 72.
Borel, Émile, 73.
Bouquet, 7.
Briot, 7.
Brodén, 73.
Brouwer, 208.
Burali-Forti, Cesare, 205, 206.

Cantor, Georg, v, vi, vii, 3, 9, 10,
    13, 18, 22, 24, 25, 26, 28,
    29, 30, 32, 33, 34, 35, 36,
    37, 38, 41, 42, 45, 46, 47,
    48, 49, 51, 52, 53, 54, 55,
    56, 57, 59, 60, 62, 63, 64,
    68, 69, 70, 72, 73, 74, 76,
    77, 79, 80, 81, 82, 202,
    204, 205, 206, 208.
Dedekind axiom, 30.
Cardinal number (*see also* Power),
    74, 79 ff., 85 ff., 202.
  finite, 97 ff.
  smallest transfinite, 103 ff.
Cardinal numbers, operations
    with, 204.
  series of transfinite, 109.
Cauchy, Augustin Louis, 2, 3, 4, 6,
    8, 12, 14, 15, 16, 17, 22, 24.
Class of types, 114.
Closed aggregates, 132.
  types, 133.
Coherences, 73.
Coherent series, 129, 130.
Commutative law with transfinite
    numbers, 66, 92, 93,
    119 ff., 190 ff.
Condensation of singularities, 3,
    9, 48, 49.
Connected aggregates, 72.
Content of aggregates, 73.
Content-less, 51.
Continuity of a function, 1.
Continuous motion in discon-
    tinuous space, 37.
Continuum, 33, 37, 41 ff., 47, 48,
    64, 70 ff., 96, 205.
Contradiction, Russell's, 206, 207.
Convergence of series, 1, 15, 16,
    17, 20, 24.
Cords, vibrating, problem of, 4.

D'Alembert (*see* Alembert, J. L. d').
Dedekind, Richard, vii, 23, 41, 47, 49, 73.
Definition of aggregate, 37.
Democritus, 70.
De Morgan, Augustus, 41.
Density in itself, 132.
Derivatives of point-aggregates, 3, 30 ff., 37.
Descartes, René, 55.
Dirichlet, Peter Gustav Lejeune, 2, 3, 5, 7, 8, 9, 22, 35.
Discrete aggregates, 51.
Distributive law with transfinite numbers, 66, 93, 121, 155.

Enumerability, 32, 38 ff., 47, 50 ff., 62.
Enumeral, 52, 62.
Epicurus, 70.
Epimenides, 207.
Equivalence of aggregates, 40, 75, 86 ff.
Euler, Leonhard, 4, 5, 9, 10.
Everywhere-dense aggregates, 33, 35, 37, 123.
types, 133.
Exponentiation of transfinite numbers, 82, 94 ff., 207.

Fontenelle, 118.
Formalism in mathematics, 70, 81.
Fourier, Jean Baptiste Joseph, 1, 2, 5, 6, 8, 24.
Freedom in mathematics, 67 ff.
Frege, Gottlob, 23, 70, 202.
Function, conception of, 1.
Functions, theory of analytic, 2, 6, 7, 10, 11, 12, 13, 22, 73.
arbitrary, 4, 6, 34.
theory of real, 2, 8, 9, 73.
Fundamental series, 26, 128 ff.

Gauss, Carl Friedrich, 6, 12, 14.
Generation, principles of, 56, 57.
Gudermann, 10.

Hahn, H., 203.
Haller, Albrecht von, 62.

Hankel, Hermann, 3, 7, 8, 9, 17, 49, 70.
Hardy, G. H., 205, 206.
Harnack, Axel, 51, 73.
Hausdorff, Felix, 207, 208.
Heine, H. E., 3, 26, 69.
Helmholtz, H. von, 42, 70, 81.
Hessenberg, Gerhard, 207.
Hobbes, Thomas, 55.

Imaginaries, 6.
Induction, mathematical, 207.
Infinite, definition of, 41, 61, 62.
Infinitesimals, 64, 81.
Infinity, proper and improper, 55, 79.
Integrability, Riemann's conditions of, 8.
Integrable aggregates, 51.
Inverse types, 114.
Irrational numbers, 3, 14 ff., 26 ff.
analogy of transfinite numbers with, 77 ff.
Isolated aggregate, 49.
point, 30.

Jacobi, C. G. J., 10.
Jordan, Camille, 73.
Jourdain, Philip E. B., 4, 6, 20, 32, 52, 205, 206, 207, 208.

Killing, W., 118.
Kind of a point-aggregate, 32.
Kirchhoff, G., 69.
König, Julius, 207.
Kronecker, L., 70, 81.
Kummer, E. E., 69.

Lagrange, J. L., 5, 14.
Leibniz, G. W. von, 55.
Leucippus, 70.
Limitation, principle of, 60.
Limiting element of an aggregate, 131.
Limit-point, 30.
Limits with transfinite numbers, 77 ff., 131 ff., 58 ff.
Liouville, J., 40.
Lipschitz, R., 6.
Locke, J., 55.
Lucretius, 70.

Mach, Ernst, 69.
Maximum of a function, 22.
Mittag-Leffler, Gosta, 11.
Mutliplication of cardinal numbers, 80, 91 ff.
  of ordinal types 81, 119 ff, 154.
  of transfinite numbers, 63, 64, 66, 176 ff.

Newton, Sir Isaac, 15.
Nominalism, Cantor's, 69, 70.
Number-concept, logical definition of, 202, 203.

Ordinal number (*see also* Enumeral), 75, 151 ff.
  numbers, finite, 113, 158, 159.
  type, 75, 79 ff., 110 ff.
  type of aggregate of rational numbers, 122 ff., 202.
  types of multiply ordered aggregates, 81, 208.
Osgood, W. F., 73.

Peano, G., 23.
Perfect aggregates, 72, 132.
  types, 133.
Philosophical revolution brought about by Cantor's work, vi.
Physical conceptions and modern mathematics, 1.
Point-aggregates, Cantor's early work on, v, vi.
  theory of, 3, 20 ff., 30 ff., 64, 73.
Potential, theory of, 7.
Power, second, 64 ff., 169 ff.
  of an aggregate, 32, 37, 40, 52 ff., 60, 62.
Prime numbers, transfinite, 64, 66.
Principal element of an aggregate, 131.
Puiseux, V., 7.

Reducible aggregates, 71.
Relation numbers, 203.
Riemann, G. F. B., 3, 7, 8, 9, 10, 12, 25, 42.

Riess, F., 208.
Russell, Bertrand, 20, 23, 53, 202, 203, 204, 206, 207.

Schepp, A., 117.
Schmidt, E., 204.
Schoenflies, A., 73, 203, 207.
Schwarz, 8, 12.
Second number-class, cardinal number of, 169 ff.
  epsilon-numbers of the, 195 ff.
  exponentiation in, 178 ff.
  normal form of numbers of, 183 ff.
  numbers of, 160 ff.
Segment of a series, 60, 103, 141 ff.
Selections, 204 ff.
Similarity, 76, 112 ff.
Species of a point-aggregate, 31.
Spinoza, B., 55.
Steiner, J., 40.
Stolz, O., 17, 73.
Subtraction of transfinite numbers, 66, 155, 156.

Teubner, B. G., vii.
Transfinite numbers, 4, 32, 36, 50 ff., 52 ff.
Trigonometrical developments, 2, 3, 4, 5, 6, 7, 8, 24 ff., 31.

Unextended aggregates, 51.
Upper limit, 21.

Veronese, G., 117, 118.

Weierstrass, Karl, vi, vii, 2, 3, 10, 11, 12, 13, 14, 17, 18, 19, 20, 21, 22, 23, 24, 26, 30, 48.
Well-ordered aggregates, 60, 61, 75 ff., 137 ff.
Well-ordering, 204 ff.
Whitehead, A. N., 203, 204.

Zeno, 15.
Zermelo, E., 204, 206, 207, 208.
Zermelo's axiom, 204 ff.

Catalogue of Dover
SCIENCE BOOKS

BOOKS THAT EXPLAIN SCIENCE

THE NATURE OF LIGHT AND COLOUR IN THE OPEN AIR, M. Minnaert. Why is falling snow sometimes black? What causes mirages, the fata morgana, multiple suns and moons in the sky; how are shadows formed? Prof. Minnaert of U. of Utrecht answers these and similar questions in optics, light, colour, for non-specialists. Particularly valuable to nature, science students, painters, photographers. "Can best be described in one word—fascinating!" Physics Today. Translated by H. M. Kremer-Priest, K. Jay. 202 illustrations, including 42 photos. xvi + 362pp. 5⅜ x 8.   T196 Paperbound **$1.95**

THE RESTLESS UNIVERSE, Max Born. New enlarged version of this remarkably readable account by a Nobel laureate. Moving from sub-atomic particles to universe, the author explains in very simple terms the latest theories of wave mechanics. Partial contents: air and its relatives, electrons and ions, waves and particles, electronic structure of the atom, nuclear physics. Nearly 1000 illustrations, including 7 animated sequences. 325pp. 6 x 9.   T412 Paperbound **$2.00**

MATTER AND LIGHT, THE NEW PHYSICS, L. de Broglie. Non-technical papers by a Nobel laureate explain electromagnetic theory, relativity, matter, light, radiation, wave mechanics, quantum physics, philosophy of science. Einstein, Planck, Bohr, others explained so easily that no mathematical training is needed for all but 2 of the 21 chapters. "Easy simplicity and lucidity . . . should make this source-book of modern physcis available to a wide public," Saturday Review. Unabridged. 300pp. 5⅜ x 8.   T35 Paperbound **$1.60**

THE COMMON SENSE OF THE EXACT SCIENCES, W. K. Clifford. Introduction by James Newman, edited by Karl Pearson. For 70 years this has been a guide to classical scientific, mathematical thought. Explains with unusual clarity basic concepts such as extension of meaning of symbols, characteristics of surface boundaries, properties of plane figures, vectors, Cartesian method of determining position, etc. Long preface by Bertrand Russell. Bibliography of Clifford. Corrected. 130 diagrams redrawn. 249pp. 5⅜ x 8.
T61 Paperbound **$1.60**

THE EVOLUTION OF SCIENTIFIC THOUGHT FROM NEWTON TO EINSTEIN, A. d'Abro. Einstein's special, general theories of relativity, with historical implications, analyzed in non-technical terms. Excellent accounts of contributions of Newton, Riemann, Weyl, Planck, Eddington, Maxwell, Lorentz, etc., are treated in terms of space, time, equations of electromagnetics, finiteness of universe, methodology of science. "Has become a standard work," Nature. 21 diagrams. 482pp. 5⅜ x 8.   T2 Paperbound **$2.00**

BRIDGES AND THEIR BUILDERS, D. Steinman, S. R. Watson. Engineers, historians, everyone ever fascinated by great spans will find this an endless source of information and interest. Dr. Steinman, recent recipient of Louis Levy Medal, is one of the great bridge architects, engineers of all time. His analysis of great bridges of history is both authoritative and easily followed. Greek, Roman, medieval, oriental bridges; modern works such as Brooklyn Bridge, Golden Gate Bridge, etc. described in terms of history, constructional principles, artistry, function. Most comprehensive, accurate semi-popular history of bridges in print in English. New, greatly revised, enlarged edition. 23 photographs, 26 line drawings. xvii + 401pp. 5⅜ x 8.   T431 Paperbound **$1.95**

CONCERNING THE NATURE OF THINGS, Sir William Bragg. Christmas lectures at Royal Society by Nobel laureate, dealing with atoms, gases, liquids, and various types of crystals. No scientific background is needed to understand this remarkably clear introduction to basic processes and aspects of modern science. "More interesting than any bestseller," London Morning Post. 32pp. of photos. 57 figures. xii + 232pp. 5⅜ x 8. **T31 Paperbound $1.35**

THE RISE OF THE NEW PHYSICS, A. d'Abro. Half million word exposition, formerly titled "The Decline of Mechanism," for readers not versed in higher mathematics. Only thorough explanation in everyday language of core of modern mathematical physical theory, treating both classical, modern views. Scientifically impeccable coverage of thought from Newtonian system through theories of Dirac, Heisenberg, Fermi's statistics. Combines history, exposition; broad but unified, detailed view, with constant comparison of classical, modern views. "A must for anyone doing serious study in the physical sciences," J. of the Franklin Inst. "Extraordinary faculty . . . to explain ideas and theories . . . in language of everyday life," Isis. Part I of set: philosophy of science, from practice of Newton, Maxwell, Poincaré, Einstein, etc. Modes of thought, experiment, causality, etc. Part II: 100 pp. on grammar, vocabulary of mathematics, discussions of functions, groups, series, Fourier series, etc. Remainder treats concrete, detailed coverage of both classical, quantum physics: analytic mechanics, Hamilton's principle, electromagnetic waves, thermodynamics, Brownian movement, special relativity, Bohr's atom, de Broglie's wave mechanics, Heisenberg's uncertainty, scores of other important topics. Covers discoveries, theories of d'Alembert, Born, Cantor, Debye, Euler, Foucault, Galois, Gauss, Hadamard, Kelvin, Kepler Laplace, Maxwell, Pauli, Rayleigh Volterra, Weyl, more than 180 others. 97 illustrations. ix + 982pp. 5⅜ x 8.
T3 Vol. 1 Paperbound $2.00
T4 Vol. II Paperbound $2.00

SPINNING TOPS AND GYROSCOPIC MOTION, John Perry. Well-known classic of science still unsurpassed for lucid, accurate, delightful exposition. How quasi-rigidity is induced in flexible, fluid bodies by rapid motions; why gyrostat falls, top rises; nature, effect of internal fluidity on rotating bodies; etc. Appendixes describe practical use of gyroscopes in ships, compasses, monorail transportation. 62 figures. 128pp. 5⅜ x 8.
T416 Paperbound $1.00

FOUNDATIONS OF PHYSICS, R. B. Lindsay, H. Margenau. Excellent bridge between semi-popular and technical writings. Discussion of methods of physical description, construction of theory; valuable to physicist with elementary calculus. Gives meaning to data, tools of modern physics. Contents: symbolism, mathematical equations; space and time; foundations of mechanics; probability; physics, continua; electron theory; relativity; quantum mechanics; causality; etc. "Thorough and yet not overdetailed. Unreservedly recommended," Nature. Unabridged corrected edition. 35 illustrations. xi + 537pp. 5⅜ x 8. **S377 Paperbound $2.45**

FADS AND FALLACIES IN THE NAME OF SCIENCE, Martin Gardner. Formerly entitled "In the Name of Science," the standard account of various cults, quack systems, delusions which have masqueraded as science: hollow earth fanatics, orgone sex energy, dianetics, Atlantis, Forteanism, flying saucers, medical fallacies like zone therapy, etc. New chapter on Bridey Murphy, psionics, other recent manifestations. A fair reasoned appraisal of eccentric theory which provides excellent innoculation. "Should be read by everyone, scientist or non-scientist alike," R. T. Birge, Prof. Emeritus of Physics, Univ. of Calif; Former Pres., Amer. Physical Soc. x + 365pp. 5⅜ x 8. **T394 Paperbound $1.50**

ON MATHEMATICS AND MATHEMATICIANS, R. E. Moritz. A 10 year labor of love by discerning, discriminating Prof. Moritz, this collection conveys the full sense of mathematics and personalities of great mathematicians. Anecdotes, aphorisms, reminiscences, philosophies, definitions, speculations, biographical insights, etc. by great mathematicians, writers: Descartes, Mill, Locke, Kant, Coleridge, Whitehead, etc. Glimpses into lives of great mathematicians, from Archimedes to Euler, Gauss, Weierstrass. To mathematicians, a superb browsing-book. To laymen, exciting revelation of fullness of mathematics. Extensive cross index. 410pp. 5⅜ x 8. **T489 Paperbound $1.95**

GUIDE TO THE LITERATURE OF MATHEMATICS AND PHYSICS, N. G. Parke III. Over 5000 entries under approximately 120 major subject headings, of selected most important books, monographs, periodicals, articles in English, plus important works in German, French, Italian, Spanish, Russian (many recently available works). Covers every branch of physics, math, related engineering. Includes author, title, edition, publisher, place, date, number of volumes, number of pages. 40 page introduction on basic problems of research, study provides useful information on organization, use of libraries, psychology of learning, etc. Will save you hours of time. 2nd revised edition. Indices of authors, subjects. 464pp. 5⅜ x 8. **S447 Paperbound $2.49**

THE STRANGE STORY OF THE QUANTUM, An Account for the General Reader of the Growth of Ideas Underlying Our Present Atomic Knowledge, B. Hoffmann. Presents lucidly, expertly, with barest amount of mathematics, problems and theories which led to modern quantum physics. Begins with late 1800's when discrepancies were noticed; with illuminating analogies, examples, goes through concepts of Planck, Einstein, Pauli, Schroedinger, Dirac, Sommerfield, Feynman, etc. New postscript through 1958. "Of the books attempting an account of the history and contents of modern atomic physics which have come to my attention, this is the best," H. Margenau, Yale U., in Amer. J. of Physics. 2nd edition. 32 tables, illustrations. 275pp. 5⅜ x 8. **T518 Paperbound $1.45**

2

HISTORY OF SCIENCE
AND PHILOSOPHY OF SCIENCE

THE VALUE OF SCIENCE, Henri Poincaré. Many of most mature ideas of "last scientific universalist" for both beginning, advanced workers. Nature of scientific truth, whether order is innate in universe or imposed by man, logical thought vs. intuition (relating to Weierstrass, Lie, Riemann, etc), time and space (relativity, psychological time, simultaneity), Herz's concept of force, values within disciplines of Maxwell, Carnot, Mayer, Newton, Lorentz, etc. iii + 147pp. 5⅜ x 8. S469 Paperbound **$1.35**

PHILOSOPHY AND THE PHYSICISTS, L. S. Stebbing. Philosophical aspects of modern science examined in terms of lively critical attack on ideas of Jeans, Eddington. Tasks of science, causality, determinism, probability, relation of world physics to that of everyday experience, philosophical significance of Planck-Bohr concept of discontinuous energy levels, inferences to be drawn from Uncertainty Principle, implications of "becoming" involved in 2nd law of thermodynamics, other problems posed by discarding of Laplacean determinism. 285pp. 5⅜ x 8. T480 Paperbound **$1.65**

THE PRINCIPLES OF SCIENCE, A TREATISE ON LOGIC AND THE SCIENTIFIC METHOD, W. S. Jevons. Milestone in development of symbolic logic remains stimulating contribution to investigation of inferential validity in sciences. Treats inductive, deductive logic, theory of number, probability, limits of scientific method; significantly advances Boole's logic, contains detailed introduction to nature and methods of probability in physics, astronomy, everyday affairs, etc. In introduction, Ernest Nagel of Columbia U. says, "[Jevons] continues to be of interest as an attempt to articulate the logic of scientific inquiry." liii + 786pp. 5⅜ x 8. S446 Paperbound **$2.98**

A HISTORY OF ASTRONOMY FROM THALES TO KEPLER, J. L. E. Dreyer. Only work in English to give complete history of cosmological views from prehistoric times to Kepler. Partial contents: Near Eastern astronomical systems, Early Greeks, Homocentric spheres of Euxodus, Epicycles, Ptolemaic system, Medieval cosmology, Copernicus, Kepler, much more. "Especially useful to teachers and students of the history of science . . . unsurpassed in its field," Isis. Formerly "A History of Planetary Systems from Thales to Kepler." Revised foreword by W. H. Stahl. xvii + 430pp. 5⅜ x 8. S79 Paperbound **$1.98**

A CONCISE HISTORY OF MATHEMATICS, D. Struik. Lucid study of development of ideas, techniques, from Ancient Near East, Greece, Islamic science, Middle Ages, Renaissance, modern times. Important mathematicians described in detail. Treatment not anecdotal, but analytical development of ideas. Non-technical—no math training needed. "Rich in content, thoughtful in interpretations," U.S. Quarterly Booklist. 60 illustrations including Greek, Egyptian manuscripts, portraits of 31 mathematicians. 2nd edition. xix + 299pp. 5⅜ x 8. S255 Paperbound **$1.75**

THE PHILOSOPHICAL WRITINGS OF PEIRCE, edited by Justus Buchler. A carefully balanced expositon of Peirce's complete system, written by Peirce himself. It covers such matters as scientific method, pure chance vs. law, symbolic logic, theory of signs, pragmatism, experiment, and other topics. "Excellent selection . . . gives more than adequate evidence of the range and greatness," Personalist. Formerly entitled "The Philosophy of Peirce." xvi + 368pp. T217 Paperbound **$1.95**

SCIENCE AND METHOD, Henri Poincaré. Procedure of scientific discovery, methodology, experiment, idea-germination—processes by which discoveries come into being. Most significant and interesting aspects of development, application of ideas. Chapters cover selection of facts, chance, mathematical reasoning, mathematics and logic; Whitehead, Russell, Cantor, the new mechanics, etc. 288pp. 5⅜ x 8. S222 Paperbound **$1.35**

SCIENCE AND HYPOTHESIS, Henri Poincaré. Creative psychology in science. How such concepts as number, magnitude, space, force, classical mechanics developed, how modern scientist uses them in his thought. Hypothesis in physics, theories of modern physics. Introduction by Sir James Larmor. "Few mathematicians have had the breadth of vision of Poincaré, and none is his superior in the gift of clear exposition," E. T. Bell. 272pp. 5⅜ x 8. S221 Paperbound **$1.35**

ESSAYS IN EXPERIMENTAL LOGIC, John Dewey. Stimulating series of essays by one of most influential minds in American philosophy presents some of his most mature thoughts on wide range of subjects. Partial contents: Relationship between inquiry and experience; dependence of knowledge upon thought; character logic; judgments of practice, data, and meanings; stimuli of thought, etc. viii + 444pp. 5⅜ x 8. T73 Paperbound **$1.95**

WHAT IS SCIENCE, Norman Campbell. Excellent introduction explains scientific method, role of mathematics, types of scientific laws. Contents: 2 aspects of science, science and nature, laws of chance, discovery of laws, explanation of laws, measurement and numerical laws, applications of science. 192pp. 5⅜ x 8. S43 Paperbound **$1.25**

3

FROM EUCLID TO EDDINGTON: A STUDY OF THE CONCEPTIONS OF THE EXTERNAL WORLD, Sir Edmund Whittaker. Foremost British scientist traces development of theories of natural philosophy from western rediscovery of Euclid to Eddington, Einstein, Dirac, etc. 5 major divisions: Space, Time and Movement; Concepts of Classical Physics; Concepts of Quantum Mechanics; Eddington Universe. Contrasts inadequacy of classical physics to understand physical world with present day attempts of relativity, non-Euclidean geometry, space curvature, etc. 212pp. 5⅜ x 8.
T491 Paperbound **$1.35**

THE ANALYSIS OF MATTER, Bertrand Russell. How do our senses accord with the new physics? This volume covers such topics as logical analysis of physics, prerelativity physics, causality, scientific inference, physics and perception, special and general relativity, Weyl's theory, tensors, invariants and their physical interpretation, periodicity and qualitative series. "The most thorough treatment of the subject that has yet been published," The Nation. Introduction by L. E. Denonn. 422pp. 5⅜ x 8.
T231 Paperbound **$1.95**

LANGUAGE, TRUTH, AND LOGIC, A. Ayer. A clear introduction to the Vienna and Cambridge schools of Logical Positivism. Specific tests to evaluate validity of ideas, etc. Contents: function of philosophy, elimination of metaphysics, nature of analysis, a priori, truth and probability, etc. 10th printing. "I should like to have written it myself," Bertrand Russell. 160pp. 5⅜ x 8.
T10 Paperbound **$1.25**

THE PSYCHOLOGY OF INVENTION IN THE MATHEMATICAL FIELD, J. Hadamard. Where do ideas come from? What role does the unconscious play? Are ideas best developed by mathematical reasoning, word reasoning, visualization? What are the methods used by Einstein, Poincaré, Galton, Riemann? How can these techniques be applied by others? One of the world's leading mathematicians discusses these and other questions. xiii + 145pp. 5⅜ x 8.
T107 Paperbound **$1.25**

GUIDE TO PHILOSOPHY, C. E. M. Joad. By one of the ablest expositors of all time, this is not simply a history or a typological survey, but an examination of central problems in terms of answers afforded by the greatest thinkers: Plato, Aristotle, Scholastics, Leibniz, Kant, Whitehead, Russell, and many others. Especially valuable to persons in the physical sciences; over 100 pages devoted to Jeans, Eddington, and others, the philosophy of modern physics, scientific materialism, pragmatism, etc. Classified bibliography. 592pp. 5⅜ x 8.
T50 Paperbound **$2.00**

SUBSTANCE AND FUNCTION, and EINSTEIN'S THEORY OF RELATIVITY, Ernst Cassirer. Two books bound as one. Cassirer establishes a philosophy of the exact sciences that takes into consideration new developments in mathematics, shows historical connections. Partial contents: Aristotelian logic, Mill's analysis, Helmholtz and Kronecker, Russell and cardinal numbers, Euclidean vs. non-Euclidean geometry, Einstein's relativity. Bibliography. Index. xxi + 464pp. 5⅜ x 8.
T50 Paperbound **$2.00**

FOUNDATIONS OF GEOMETRY, Bertrand Russell. Nobel laureate analyzes basic problems in the overlap area between mathematics and philosophy: the nature of geometrical knowledge, the nature of geometry, and the applications of geometry to space. Covers history of non-Euclidean geometry, philosophic interpretations of geometry, especially Kant, projective and metrical geometry. Most interesting as the solution offered in 1897 by a great mind to a problem still current. New introduction by Prof. Morris Kline, N.Y. University. "Admirably clear, precise, and elegantly reasoned analysis," International Math. News. xii + 201pp. 5⅜ x 8.
S233 Paperbound **$1.60**

THE NATURE OF PHYSICAL THEORY, P. W. Bridgman. How modern physics looks to a highly unorthodox physicist—a Nobel laureate. Pointing out many absurdities of science, demonstrating inadequacies of various physical theories, weighs and analyzes contributions of Einstein, Bohr, Heisenberg, many others. A non-technical consideration of correlation of science and reality. xi + 138pp. 5⅜ x 8.
S33 Paperbound **$1.25**

EXPERIMENT AND THEORY IN PHYSICS, Max Born. A Nobel laureate examines the nature and value of the counterclaims of experiment and theory in physics. Synthetic versus analytical scientific advances are analyzed in works of Einstein, Bohr, Heisenberg, Planck, Eddington, Milne, others, by a fellow scientist. 44pp. 5⅜ x 8.
S308 Paperbound **60¢**

A SHORT HISTORY OF ANATOMY AND PHYSIOLOGY FROM THE GREEKS TO HARVEY, Charles Singer. Corrected edition of "The Evolution of Anatomy." Classic traces anatomy, physiology from prescientific times through Greek, Roman periods, dark ages, Renaissance, to beginning of modern concepts. Centers on individuals, movements, that definitely advanced anatomical knowledge. Plato, Diocles, Erasistratus, Galen, da Vinci, etc. Special section on Vesalius. 20 plates. 270 extremely interesting illustrations of ancient, Medieval, Renaissance, Oriental origin. xii + 209pp. 5⅜ x 8.
T389 Paperbound **$1.75**

SPACE - TIME - MATTER, Hermann Weyl. "The standard treatise on the general theory of relativity," (Nature), by world renowned scientist. Deep, clear discussion of logical coherence of general theory, introducing all needed tools: Maxwell, analytical geometry, non-Euclidean geometry, tensor calculus, etc. Basis is classical space-time, before absorption of relativity. Contents: Euclidean space, mathematical form, metrical continuum, general theory, etc. 15 diagrams. xviii + 330pp. 5⅜ x 8.
S267 Paperbound **$1.75**

4

DOVER SCIENCE BOOKS

MATTER AND MOTION, James Clerk Maxwell. Excellent exposition begins with simple particles, proceeds gradually to physical systems beyond complete analysis; motion, force, properties of centre of mass of material system; work, energy, gravitation, etc. Written with all Maxwell's original insights and clarity. Notes by E. Larmor. 17 diagrams. 178pp. 5⅜ x 8.　　　　　　　　　　　　　　　　　　　　　　　　　S188 Paperbound **$1.25**

PRINCIPLES OF MECHANICS, Heinrich Hertz. Last work by the great 19th century physicist is not only a classic, but of great interest in the logic of science. Creating a new system of mechanics based upon space, time, and mass, it returns to axiomatic analysis, understanding of the formal or structural aspects of science, taking into account logic, observation, a priori elements. Of great historical importance to Poincaré, Carnap, Einstein, Milne. A 20 page introduction by R. S. Cohen, Wesleyan University, analyzes the implications of Hertz's thought and the logic of science. 13 page introduction by Helmholtz. xlii + 274pp. 5⅜ x 8.　　　　　　　　　　　　　　　　　　　　　　　S316 Clothbound **$3.50**
　　　　　　　　　　　　　　　　　　　　　　　　　　　　　S317 Paperbound **$1.75**

FROM MAGIC TO SCIENCE, Charles Singer. A great historian examines aspects of science from Roman Empire through Renaissance. Includes perhaps best discussion of early herbals, penetrating physiological interpretation of "The Visions of Hildegarde of Bingen." Also examines Arabian, Galenic influences; Pythagoras' sphere, Paracelsus; reawakening of science under Leonardo da Vinci, Vesalius; Lorica of Gildas the Briton; etc. Frequent quotations with translations from contemporary manuscripts. Unabridged, corrected edition. 158 unusual illustrations from Classical, Medieval sources. xxvii + 365pp. 5⅜ x 8.　　　　　　　　　　　　　　　　　　　　　　　　　T390 Paperbound **$2.00**

A HISTORY OF THE CALCULUS, AND ITS CONCEPTUAL DEVELOPMENT, Carl B. Boyer. Provides laymen, mathematicians a detailed history of the development of the calculus, from beginnings in antiquity to final elaboration as mathematical abstraction. Gives a sense of mathematics not as technique, but as habit of mind, in progression of ideas of Zeno, Plato, Pythagoras, Eudoxus, Arabic and Scholastic mathematicians, Newton, Leibniz, Taylor, Descartes, Euler, Lagrange, Cantor, Weierstrass, and others. This first comprehensive, critical history of the calculus was originally entitled "The Concepts of the Calculus." Foreword by R. Courant. 22 figures. 25 page bibliography. v + 364pp. 5⅜ x 8.　　　　　　　　　　　　　　　　　　　　　　　　　S509 Paperbound **$2.00**

A DIDEROT PICTORIAL ENCYCLOPEDIA OF TRADES AND INDUSTRY, Manufacturing and the Technical Arts in Plates Selected from "L'Encyclopédie ou Dictionnaire Raisonné des Sciences, des Arts, et des Métiers" of Denis Diderot. Edited with text by C. Gillispie. First modern selection of plates from high-point of 18th century French engraving. Storehouse of technological information to historian of arts and science. Over 2,000 illustrations on 485 full page plates, most of them original size, show trades, industries of fascinating era in such great detail that modern reconstructions might be made of them. Plates teem with men, women, children performing thousands of operations; show sequence, general operations, closeups, details of machinery. Illustrates such important, interesting trades, industries as sowing, harvesting, beekeeping, tobacco processing, fishing, arts of war, mining, smelting, casting iron, extracting mercury, making gunpowder, cannons, bells, shoeing horses, tanning, papermaking, printing, dying, over 45 more categories. Professor Gillispie of Princeton supplies full commentary on all plates, identifies operations, tools, processes, etc. Material is presented in lively, lucid fashion. Of great interest to all studying history of science, technology. Heavy library cloth. 920pp. 9 x 12.　　　　　　　　　　　　　　　　　　　　　　　　　T421 2 volume set **$18.50**

DE MAGNETE, William Gilbert. Classic work on magnetism, founded new science. Gilbert was first to use word "electricity," to recognize mass as distinct from weight, to discover effect of heat on magnetic bodies; invented an electroscope, differentiated between static electricity and magnetism, conceived of earth as magnet. This lively work, by first great experimental scientist, is not only a valuable historical landmark, but a delightfully easy to follow record of a searching, ingenious mind. Translated by P. F. Mottelay. 25 page biographical memoir. 90 figures. lix + 368pp. 5⅜ x 8.　　　　　S470 Paperbound **$2.00**

HISTORY OF MATHEMATICS, D. E. Smith. Most comprehensive, non-technical history of math in English. Discusses lives and works of over a thousand major, minor figures, with footnotes giving technical information outside book's scheme, and indicating disputed matters. Vol. I: A chronological examination, from primitive concepts through Egypt, Babylonia, Greece, the Orient, Rome, the Middle Ages, The Renaissance, and to 1900. Vol. II: The development of ideas in specific fields and problems, up through elementary calculus. "Marks an epoch . . . will modify the entire teaching of the history of science," George Sarton. 2 volumes, total of 510 illustrations, 1355pp. 5⅜ x 8. Set boxed in attractive container.　　　　　　　　　　　　　　　　T429, 430 Paperbound, the set **$5.00**

THE PHILOSOPHY OF SPACE AND TIME, H. Reichenbach. An important landmark in development of empiricist conception of geometry, covering foundations of geometry, time theory, consequences of Einstein's relativity, including: relations between theory and observations; coordinate definitions; relations between topological and metrical properties of space; psychological problem of visual intuition of non-Euclidean structures; many more topics important to modern science and philosophy. Majority of ideas require only knowledge of intermediate math. "Still the best book in the field," Rudolf Carnap. Introduction by R. Carnap. 49 figures. xviii + 296pp. 5⅜ x 8.　　　　　　　S443 Paperbound **$2.00**

FOUNDATIONS OF SCIENCE: THE PHILOSOPHY OF THEORY AND EXPERIMENT, N. Campbell. A critique of the most fundamental concepts of science, particularly physics. Examines why certain propositions are accepted without question, demarcates science from philosophy, etc. Part I analyzes presuppositions of scientific thought: existence of material world, nature of laws, probability, etc; part 2 covers nature of experiment and applications of mathematics: conditions for measurement, relations between numerical laws and theories, error, etc. An appendix covers problems arising from relativity, force, motion, space, time. A classic in its field. "A real grasp of what science is," Higher Educational Journal. xiii + 565pp. 5⅝ x 8⅜. S372 Paperbound **$2.95**

THE STUDY OF THE HISTORY OF MATHEMATICS and **THE STUDY OF THE HISTORY OF SCIENCE, G. Sarton.** Excellent introductions, orientation, for beginning or mature worker. Describes duty of mathematical historian, incessant efforts and genius of previous generations. Explains how today's discipline differs from previous methods. 200 item bibliography with critical evaluations, best available biographies of modern mathematicians, best treatises on historical methods is especially valuable. 10 illustrations. 2 volumes bound as one. 113pp. + 75pp. 5⅜ x 8. T240 Paperbound **$1.25**

MATHEMATICAL PUZZLES

MATHEMATICAL PUZZLES OF SAM LOYD, selected and edited by **Martin Gardner.** 117 choice puzzles by greatest American puzzle creator and innovator, from his famous "Cyclopedia of Puzzles." All unique style, historical flavor of originals. Based on arithmetic, algebra, probability, game theory, route tracing, topology, sliding block, operations research, geometrical dissection. Includes famous "14-15" puzzle which was national craze, "Horse of a Different Color" which sold millions of copies. 120 line drawings, diagrams. Solutions. xx + 167pp. 5⅜ x 8. T498 Paperbound **$1.00**

SYMBOLIC LOGIC and THE GAME OF LOGIC, Lewis Carroll. "Symbolic Logic" is not concerned with modern symbolic logic, but is instead a collection of over 380 problems posed with charm and imagination, using the syllogism, and a fascinating diagrammatic method of drawing conclusions. In "The Game of Logic" Carroll's whimsical imagination devises a logical game played with 2 diagrams and counters (included) to manipulate hundreds of tricky syllogisms. The final section, "Hit or Miss" is a lagniappe of 101 additional puzzles in the delightful Carroll manner. Until this reprint edition, both of these books were rarities costing up to $15 each. Symbolic Logic: Index. xxxi + 199pp. The Game of Logic: 96pp. 2 vols. bound as one. 5⅜ x 8. T492 Paperbound **$1.50**

PILLOW PROBLEMS and A TANGLED TALE, Lewis Carroll. One of the rarest of all Carroll's works, "Pillow Problems" contains 72 original math puzzles, all typically ingenious. Particularly fascinating are Carroll's answers which remain exactly as he thought them out, reflecting his actual mental process. The problems in "A Tangled Tale" are in story form, originally appearing as a monthly magazine serial. Carroll not only gives the solutions, but uses answers sent in by readers to discuss wrong approaches and misleading paths, and grades them for insight. Both of these books were rarities until this edition, "Pillow Problems" costing up to $25, and "A Tangled Tale" $15. Pillow Problems: Preface and Introduction by Lewis Carroll. xx + 109pp. A Tangled Tale: 6 illustrations. 152pp. Two vols. bound as one. 5⅜ x 8. T493 Paperbound **$1.50**

NEW WORD PUZZLES, G. L. Kaufman. 100 brand new challenging puzzles on words, combinations, never before published. Most are new types invented by author, for beginners and experts both. Squares of letters follow chess moves to build words; symmetrical designs made of synonyms; rhymed crostics; double word squares; syllable puzzles where you fill in missing syllables instead of missing letter; many other types, all new. Solutions. "Excellent," Recreation. 100 puzzles. 196 figures. vi + 122pp. 5⅜ x 8. T344 Paperbound **$1.00**

MATHEMATICAL EXCURSIONS, H. A. Merrill. Fun, recreation, insights into elementary problem solving. Math expert guides you on by-paths not generally travelled in elementary math courses—divide by inspection, Russian peasant multiplication; memory systems for pi; odd, even magic squares; dyadic systems; square roots by geometry; Tchebichev's machine; dozens more. Solutions to more difficult ones. "Brain stirring stuff . . . a classic," Genie. 50 illustrations. 145pp. 5⅜ x 8. T350 Paperbound **$1.00**

THE BOOK OF MODERN PUZZLES, G. L. Kaufman. Over 150 puzzles, absolutely all new material based on same appeal as crosswords, deduction puzzles, but with different principles, techniques. 2-minute teasers, word labyrinths, design, pattern, logic, observation puzzles, puzzles testing ability to apply general knowledge to peculiar situations, many others. Solutions. 116 illustrations. 192pp. 5⅜ x 8. T143 Paperbound **$1.00**

MATHEMAGIC, MAGIC PUZZLES, AND GAMES WITH NUMBERS, R. V. Heath. Over 60 puzzles, stunts, on properties of numbers. Easy techniques for multiplying large numbers mentally, identifying unknown numbers, finding date of any day in any year. Includes The Lost Digit, 3 Acrobats, Psychic Bridge, magic squares, triangles, cubes, others not easily found elsewhere. Edited by J. S. Meyer. 76 illustrations. 128pp. 5⅜ x 8. T110 Paperbound **$1.00**

PUZZLE QUIZ AND STUNT FUN, J. Meyer. 238 high-priority puzzles, stunts, tricks—math puzzles like The Clever Carpenter, Atom Bomb, Please Help Alice; mysteries, deductions like The Bridge of Sighs, Secret Code; observation puzzlers like The American Flag, Playing Cards, Telephone Dial; over 200 others with magic squares, tongue twisters, puns, anagrams. Solutions. Revised, enlarged edition of "Fun-To-Do." Over 100 illustrations. 238 puzzles, stunts, tricks. 256pp. 5⅜ x 8.   **T337 Paperbound $1.00**

101 PUZZLES IN THOUGHT AND LOGIC, C. R. Wylie, Jr. For readers who enjoy challenge, stimulation of logical puzzles without specialized math or scientific knowledge. Problems entirely new, range from relatively easy to brainteasers for hours of subtle entertainment. Detective puzzles, find the lying fisherman, how a blind man identifies color by logic, many more. Easy-to-understand introduction to logic of puzzle solving and general scientific method. 128pp. 5⅜ x 8.   **T367 Paperbound $1.00**

CRYPTANALYSIS, H. F. Gaines. Standard elementary, intermediate text for serious students. Not just old material, but much not generally known, except to experts. Concealment, Transposition, Substitution ciphers; Vigenere, Kasiski, Playfair, multafid, dozens of other techniques. Formerly "Elementary Cryptanalysis." Appendix with sequence charts, letter frequencies in English, 5 other languages, English word frequencies. Bibliography. 167 codes. New to this edition: solutions to codes. vi + 230pp. 5⅜ x 8⅜.
T97 Paperbound $1.95

CRYPTOGRAPY, L. D. Smith. Excellent elementary introduction to enciphering, deciphering secret writing. Explains transposition, substitution ciphers; codes; solutions; geometrical patterns, route transcription, columnar transposition, other methods. Mixed cipher systems; single, polyalphabetical substitutions; mechanical devices; Vigenere; etc. Enciphering Japanese; explanation of Baconian biliteral cipher; frequency tables. Over 150 problems. Bibliography. Index. 164pp. 5⅜ x 8.   **T247 Paperbound $1.00**

MATHEMATICS, MAGIC AND MYSTERY, M. Gardner. Card tricks, metal mathematics, stage mind-reading, other "magic" explained as applications of probability, sets, number theory, etc. Creative examination of laws, applications. Scores of new tricks, insights. 115 sections on cards, dice, coins; vanishing tricks, many others. No sleight of hand—math guarantees success. "Could hardly get more entertainment . . . easy to follow," Mathematics Teacher. 115 illustrations. xii + 174pp. 5⅜ x 8.   **T335 Paperbound $1.00**

AMUSEMENTS IN MATHEMATICS, H. E. Dudeney. Foremost British originator of math puzzles, always witty, intriguing, paradoxical in this classic. One of largest collections. More than 430 puzzles, problems, paradoxes. Mazes, games, problems on number manipulations, unicursal, other route problems, puzzles on measuring, weighing, packing, age, kinship, chessboards, joiners', crossing river, plane figure dissection, many others. Solutions. More than 450 illustrations. viii + 258pp. 5⅜ x 8.   **T473 Paperbound $1.25**

THE CANTERBURY PUZZLES H. E. Dudeney. Chaucer's pilgrims set one another problems in story form. Also Adventures of the Puzzle Club, the Strange Escape of the King's Jester, the Monks of Riddlewell, the Squire's Christmas Puzzle Party, others. All puzzles are original, based on dissecting plane figures, arithmetic, algebra, elementary calculus, other branches of mathematics, and purely logical ingenuity. "The limit of ingenuity and intricacy," The Observer. Over 110 puzzles, full solutions. 150 illustrations. viii + 225 pp. 5⅜ x 8.   **T474 Paperbound $1.25**

MATHEMATICAL PUZZLES FOR BEGINNERS AND ENTHUSIASTS, G. Mott-Smith. 188 puzzles to test mental agility. Inference, interpretation, algebra, dissection of plane figures, geometry, properties of numbers, decimation, permutations, probability, all are in these delightful problems. Includes the Odic Force, How to Draw an Ellipse, Spider's Cousin, more than 180 others. Detailed solutions. Appendix with square roots, triangular numbers, primes, etc. 135 illustrations. 2nd revised edition. 248pp. 5⅜ x 8.   **T198 Paperbound $1.00**

MATHEMATICAL RECREATIONS, M. Kraitchik. Some 250 puzzles, problems, demonstrations of recreation mathematics on relatively advanced level. Unusual historical problems from Greek, Medieval, Arabic, Hindu sources; modern problems on "mathematics without numbers," geometry, topology, arithmetic, etc. Pastimes derived from figurative, Mersenne, Fermat numbers; fairy chess; latruncles: reversi; etc. Full solutions. Excellent insights into special fields of math. "Strongly recommended to all who are interested in the lighter side of mathematics," Mathematical Gaz. 181 illustrations. 330pp. 5⅜ x 8.
T163 Paperbound $1.75

FICTION

FLATLAND, E. A. Abbott. A perennially popular science-fiction classic about life in a 2-dimensional world, and the impingement of higher dimensions. Political, satiric, humorous, moral overtones. This land where women are straight lines and the lowest and most dangerous classes are isosceles triangles with 3° vertices conveys brilliantly a feeling for many concepts of modern science. 7th edition. New introduction by Banesh Hoffmann. 128pp. 5⅜ x 8.   **T1 Paperbound $1.00**

SEVEN SCIENCE FICTION NOVELS OF H. G. WELLS. Complete texts, unabridged, of seven of Wells' greatest novels: The War of the Worlds, The Invisible Man, The Island of Dr. Moreau, The Food of the Gods, First Men in the Moon, In the Days of the Comet, The Time Machine. Still considered by many experts to be the best science-fiction ever written, they will offer amusements and instruction to the scientific minded reader. "The great master," Sky and Telescope. 1051pp. 5⅜ x 8.   T264 Clothbound **$3.95**

28 SCIENCE FICTION STORIES OF H. G. WELLS. Unabridged! This enormous omnibus contains 2 full length novels—Men Like Gods, Star Begotten—plus 26 short stories of space, time, invention, biology, etc. The Crystal Egg, The Country of the Blind, Empire of the Ants, The Man Who Could Work Miracles, Aepyornis Island, A Story of the Days to Come, and 20 others "A master . . . not surpassed by . . . writers of today," The English Journal. 915pp. 5⅜ x 8.   T265 Clothbound **$3.95**

FIVE ADVENTURE NOVELS OF H. RIDER HAGGARD. All the mystery and adventure of darkest Africa captured accurately by a man who lived among Zulus for years, who knew African ethnology, folkways as did few of his contemporaries. They have been regarded as examples of the very best high adventure by such critics as Orwell, Andrew Lang, Kipling. Contents: She, King Solomon's Mines, Allan Quatermain, Allan's Wife, Maiwa's Revenge. "Could spin a yarn so full of suspense and color that you couldn't put the story down," Sat. Review. 821pp. 5⅜ x 8.   T108 Clothbound **$3.95**

CHESS AND CHECKERS

LEARN CHESS FROM THE MASTERS, Fred Reinfeld. Easiest, most instructive way to improve your game—play 10 games against such masters as Marshall, Znosko-Borovsky, Bronstein, Najdorf, etc., with each move graded by easy system. Includes ratings for alternate moves possible. Games selected for interest, clarity, easily isolated principles. Covers Ruy Lopez, Dutch Defense, Vienna Game openings; subtle, intricate middle game variations; all-important end game. Full annotations. Formerly "Chess by Yourself." 91 diagrams. viii + 144pp. 5⅜ x 8.   T362 Paperbound **$1.00**

REINFELD ON THE END GAME IN CHESS, Fred Reinfeld. Analyzes 62 end games by Alekhine, Flohr, Tarrasch, Morphy, Capablanca, Rubinstein, Lasker, Reshevsky, other masters. Only 1st rate book with extensive coverage of error—tell exactly what is wrong with each move you might have made. Centers around transitions from middle play to end play. King and pawn, minor pieces, queen endings; blockage, weak, passed pawns, etc. "Excellent . . . a boon," Chess Life. Formerly "Practical End Play." 62 figures. vi + 177pp. 5⅜ x 8.
T417 Paperbound **$1.25**

HYPERMODERN CHESS as developed in the games of its greatest exponent, ARON NIMZO-VICH, edited by Fred Reinfeld. An intensely original player, analyst, Nimzovich's approaches startled, often angered the chess world. This volume, designed for the average player, shows how his iconoclastic methods won him victories over Alekhine, Lasker, Marshall, Rubinstein, Spielmann, others, and infused new life into the game. Use his methods to startle opponents, invigorate play. "Annotations and introductions to each game . . . are excellent," Times (London). 180 diagrams. viii + 220pp. 5⅜ x 8.   T448 Paperbound **$1.35**

THE ADVENTURE OF CHESS, Edward Lasker. Lively reader, by one of America's finest chess masters, including: history of chess, from ancient Indian 4-handed game of Chaturanga to great players of today; such delights and oddities as Maelzel's chess-playing automaton that beat Napoleon 3 times; etc. One of most valuable features is author's personal recollections of men he has played against—Nimzovich, Emanuel Lasker, Capablanca, Alekhine, etc. Discussion of chess-playing machines (newly revised). 5 page chess primer. 11 illustrations. 53 diagrams. 296pp. 5⅜ x 8.   S510 Paperbound **$1.45**

THE ART OF CHESS, James Mason. Unabridged reprinting of latest revised edition of most famous general study ever written. Mason, early 20th century master, teaches beginning, intermediate player over 90 openings; middle game, end game, to see more moves ahead, to plan purposefully, attack, sacrifice, defend, exchange, govern general strategy. "Classic . . . one of the clearest and best developed studies," Publishers Weekly. Also included, a complete supplement by F. Reinfeld, "How Do You Play Chess?", invaluable to beginners for its lively question-and-answer method. 448 diagrams. 1947 Reinfeld-Bernstein text. Bibliography. xvi + 340pp. 5⅜ x 8.   T463 Paperbound **$1.85**

MORPHY'S GAMES OF CHESS, edited by P. W. Sergeant. Put boldness into your game by flowing brilliant, forceful moves of the greatest chess player of all time. 300 of Morphy's best games, carefully annotated to reveal principles. 54 classics against masters like Anderssen, Harrwitz, Bird, Paulsen, and others. 52 games at odds; 54 blindfold games; plus over 100 others. Follow his interpretation of Dutch Defense, Evans Gambit, Giuoco Piano, Ruy Lopez, many more. Unabridged reissue of latest revised edition. New introduction by F. Reinfeld. Annotations, introduction by Sergeant. 235 diagrams. x + 352pp. 5⅜ x 8.
T386 Paperbound **$1.75**

DOVER SCIENCE BOOKS

WIN AT CHECKERS, M. Hopper. (Formerly "Checkers.") Former World's Unrestricted Checker Champion discusses principles of game, expert's shots, traps, problems for beginner, standard openings, locating best move, end game, opening "blitzkrieg" moves to draw when behind, etc. Over 100 detailed questions, answers anticipate problems. Appendix. 75 problems with solutions, diagrams. 79 figures. xi + 107pp. 5⅜ x 8.   T363 Paperbound **$1.00**

HOW TO FORCE CHECKMATE, Fred Reinfeld. If you have trouble finishing off your opponent, here is a collection of lightning strokes and combinations from actual tournament play. Starts with 1-move checkmates, works up to 3-move mates. Develops ability to look ahead, gain new insights into combinations, complex or deceptive positions; ways to estimate weaknesses, strengths of you and your opponent. "A good deal of amusement and instruction," Times, (London). 300 diagrams. Solutions to all positions. Formerly "Challenge to Chess Players." 111pp. 5⅜ x 8.   T417 Paperbound **$1.25**

A TREASURY OF CHESS LORE, edited by Fred Reinfeld. Delightful collection of anecdotes, short stories, aphorisms by, about masters; poems, accounts of games, tournaments, photographs; hundreds of humorous, pithy, satirical, wise, historical episodes, comments, word portraits. Fascinating "must" for chess players; revealing and perhaps seductive to those who wonder what their friends see in game. 49 photographs (14 full page plates). 12 diagrams. xi + 306pp. 5⅜ x 8.   T458 Paperbound **$1.75**

WIN AT CHESS, Fred Reinfeld. 300 practical chess situations, to sharpen your eye, test skill against masters. Start with simple examples, progress at own pace to complexities. This selected series of crucial moments in chess will stimulate imagination, develop stronger, more versatile game. Simple grading system enables you to judge progress. "Extensive use of diagrams is a great attraction," Chess. 300 diagrams. Notes, solutions to every situation. Formerly "Chess Quiz." vi + 120pp. 5⅜ x 8.   T433 Paperbound **$1.00**

MATHEMATICS:
ELEMENTARY TO INTERMEDIATE

HOW TO CALCULATE QUICKLY, H. Sticker. Tried and true method to help mathematics of everyday life. Awakens "number sense"—ability to see relationships between numbers as whole quantities. A serious course of over 9000 problems and their solutions through techniques not taught in schools: left-to-right multiplications, new fast division, etc. 10 minutes a day will double or triple calculation speed. Excellent for scientist at home in higher math, but dissatisfied with speed and accuracy in lower math. 256pp. 5 x 7¼.
Paperbound **$1.00**

FAMOUS PROBLEMS OF ELEMENTARY GEOMETRY, Felix Klein. Expanded version of 1894 Easter lectures at Göttingen. 3 problems of classical geometry: squaring the circle, trisecting angle, doubling cube, considered with full modern implications: transcendental numbers, pi, etc. "A modern classic . . . no knowledge of higher mathematics is required," Scientia. Notes by R. Archibald. 16 figures. xi + 92pp. 5⅜ x 8.   T298 Paperbound **$1.00**

HIGHER MATHEMATICS FOR STUDENTS OF CHEMISTRY AND PHYSICS, J. W. Mellor. Practical, not abstract, building problems out of familiar laboratory material. Covers differential calculus, coordinate, analytical geometry, functions, integral calculus, infinite series, numerical equations, differential equations, Fourier's theorem probability, theory of errors, calculus of variations, determinants. "If the reader is not familiar with this book, it will repay him to examine it," Chem. and Engineering News. 800 problems. 189 figures. xxi + 641pp. 5⅜ x 8.   S193 Paperbound **$2.25**

TRIGONOMETRY REFRESHER FOR TECHNICAL MEN, A. A. Klaf. 913 detailed questions, answers cover most important aspects of plane, spherical trigonometry—particularly useful in clearing up difficulties in special areas. Part I: plane trig, angles, quadrants, functions, graphical representation, interpolation, equations, logs, solution of triangle, use of slide rule, etc. Next 188 pages discuss applications to navigation, surveying, elasticity, architecture, other special fields. Part 3: spherical trig, applications to terrestrial, astronomical problems. Methods of time-saving, simplification of principal angles, make book most useful. 913 questions answered. 1738 problems, answers to odd numbers. 494 figures. 24 pages of formulas, functions. x + 629pp. 5⅜ x 8.   T371 Paperbound **$2.00**

CALCULUS REFRESHER FOR TECHNICAL MEN, A. A. Klaf. 756 questions examine most important aspects of integral, differential calculus. Part I: simple differential calculus, constants, variables, functions, increments, logs, curves, etc. Part 2: fundamental ideas of integrations, inspection, substitution, areas, volumes, mean value, double, triple integration, etc. Practical aspects stressed. 50 pages illustrate applications to specific problems of civil, nautical engineering, electricity, stress, strain, elasticity, similar fields. 756 questions answered. 566 problems, mostly answered. 36pp. of useful constants, formulas. v + 431pp. 5⅜ x 8.   T370 Paperbound **$2.00**

MONOGRAPHS ON TOPICS OF MODERN MATHEMATICS, edited by J. W. A. Young. Advanced mathematics for persons who have forgotten, or not gone beyond, high school algebra. 9 monographs on foundation of geometry, modern pure geometry, non-Euclidean geometry, fundamental propositions of algebra, algebraic equations, functions, calculus, theory of numbers, etc. Each monograph gives proofs of important results, and descriptions of leading methods, to provide wide coverage. "Of high merit," Scientific American. New introduction by Prof. M. Kline, N.Y. Univ. 100 diagrams. xvi + 416pp. 6⅛ x 9¼.
S289 Paperbound **$2.00**

MATHEMATICS IN ACTION, O. G. Sutton. Excellent middle level application of mathematics to study of universe, demonstrates how math is applied to ballistics, theory of computing machines, waves, wave-like phenomena, theory of fluid flow, meteorological problems, statistics, flight, similar phenomena. No knowledge of advanced math required. Differential equations, Fourier series, group concepts, Eigenfunctions, Planck's constant, airfoil theory, and similar topics explained so clearly in everyday language that almost anyone can derive benefit from reading this even if much of high-school math is forgotten. 2nd edition. 88 figures. viii + 236pp. 5⅜ x 8.
T450 Clothbound **$3.50**

ELEMENTARY MATHEMATICS FROM AN ADVANCED STANDPOINT, Felix Klein. Classic text, an outgrowth of Klein's famous integration and survey course at Göttingen. Using one field to interpret, adjust another, it covers basic topics in each area, with extensive analysis. Especially valuable in areas of modern mathematics. "A great mathematician, inspiring teacher, . . . deep insight," Bul., Amer. Math Soc.

Vol. I. ARITHMETIC, ALGEBRA, ANALYSIS. Introduces concept of function immediately, enlivens discussion with graphical, geometric methods. Partial contents: natural numbers, special properties, complex numbers. Real equations with real unknowns, complex quantities. Logarithmic, exponential functions, infinitesimal calculus. Transcendence of e and pi, theory of assemblages. Index. 125 figures. ix + 274pp. 5⅜ x 8.
S151 Paperbound **$1.75**

Vol. II. GEOMETRY. Comprehensive view, accompanies space perception inherent in geometry with analytic formulas which facilitate precise formulation. Partial contents: Simplest geometric manifold; line segments, Grassman determinant principles, classification of configurations of space. Geometric transformations: affine, projective, higher point transformations, theory of the imaginary. Systematic discussion of geometry and its foundations. 141 illustrations. ix + 214pp. 5⅜ x 8.
S151 Paperbound **$1.75**

A TREATISE ON PLANE AND ADVANCED TRIGONOMETRY, E. W. Hobson. Extraordinarily wide coverage, going beyond usual college level, one of few works covering advanced trig in full detail. By a great expositor with unerring anticipation of potentially difficult points. Includes circular functions; expansion of functions of multiple angle; trig tables; relations between sides, angles of triangles; complex numbers; etc. Many problems fully solved. "The best work on the subject," Nature. Formerly entitled "A Treatise on Plane Trigonometry." 689 examples. 66 figures. xvi + 383pp. 5⅜ x 8.
S353 Paperbound **$1.95**

NON-EUCLIDEAN GEOMETRY, Roberto Bonola. The standard coverage of non-Euclidean geometry. Examines from both a historical and mathematical point of view geometries which have arisen from a study of Euclid's 5th postulate on parallel lines. Also included are complete texts, translated, of Bolyai's "Theory of Absolute Space," Lobachevsky's "Theory of Parallels." 180 diagrams. 431pp. 5⅜ x 8.
S27 Paperbound **$1.95**

GEOMETRY OF FOUR DIMENSIONS, H. P. Manning. Unique in English as a clear, concise introduction. Treatment is synthetic, mostly Euclidean, though in hyperplanes and hyperspheres at infinity, non-Euclidean geometry is used. Historical introduction. Foundations of 4-dimensional geometry. Perpendicularity, simple angles. Angles of planes, higher order. Symmetry, order, motion; hyperpyramids, hypercones, hyperspheres; figures with parallel elements; volume, hypervolume in space; regular polyhedroids. Glossary. 78 figures. ix + 348pp. 5⅜ x 8.
S182 Paperbound **$1.95**

MATHEMATICS: INTERMEDIATE TO ADVANCED

GEOMETRY (EUCLIDEAN AND NON-EUCLIDEAN)

THE GEOMETRY OF RENÉ DESCARTES. With this book, Descartes founded analytical geometry. Original French text, with Descartes's own diagrams, and excellent Smith-Latham translation. Contains: Problems the Construction of Which Requires only Straight Lines and Circles; On the Nature of Curved Lines; On the Construction of Solid or Supersolid Problems. Diagrams. 258pp. 5⅜ x 8.
S68 Paperbound **$1.50**

DOVER SCIENCE BOOKS

THE WORKS OF ARCHIMEDES, edited by T. L. Heath. All the known works of the great Greek mathematician, including the recently discovered Method of Archimedes. Contains: On Sphere and Cylinder, Measurement of a Circle, Spirals, Conoids, Spheroids, etc. Definitive edition of greatest mathematical intellect of ancient world. 186 page study by Heath discusses Archimedes and history of Greek mathematics. 563pp. 5⅜ x 8.   S9 Paperbound **$2.00**

COLLECTED WORKS OF BERNARD RIEMANN. Important sourcebook, first to contain complete text of 1892 "Werke" and the 1902 supplement, unabridged. 31 monographs, 3 complete lecture courses, 15 miscellaneous papers which have been of enormous importance in relativity, topology, theory of complex variables, other areas of mathematics. Edited by R. Dedekind, H. Weber, M. Noether, W. Wirtinger. German text; English introduction by Hans Lewy. 690pp. 5⅜ x 8.   S226 Paperbound **$2.85**

THE THIRTEEN BOOKS OF EUCLID'S ELEMENTS, edited by Sir Thomas Heath. Definitive edition of one of very greatest classics of Western world. Complete translation of Heiberg text, plus spurious Book XIV. 150 page introduction on Greek, Medieval mathematics, Euclid, texts, commentators, etc. Elaborate critical apparatus parallels text, analyzing each definition, postulate, proposition, covering textual matters, refutations, supports, extrapolations, etc. This is the full Euclid. Unabridged reproduction of Cambridge U. 2nd edition. 3 volumes. 995 figures. 1426pp. 5⅜ x 8.   S88, 89, 90, 3 volume set, paperbound **$6.00**

AN INTRODUCTION TO GEOMETRY OF N DIMENSIONS, D. M. Y. Sommerville. Presupposes no previous knowledge of field. Only book in English devoted exclusively to higher dimensional geometry. Discusses fundamental ideas of incidence, parallelism, perpendicularity, angles between linear space, enumerative geometry, analytical geometry from projective and metric views, polytopes, elementary ideas in analysis situs, content of hyperspacial figures. 60 diagrams. 196pp. 5⅜ x 8.   S494 Paperbound **$1.50**

ELEMENTS OF NON-EUCLIDEAN GEOMETRY, D. M. Y. Sommerville. Unique in proceeding step-by-step. Requires only good knowledge of high-school geometry and algebra, to grasp elementary hyperbolic, elliptic, analytic non-Euclidean Geometries; space curvature and its implications; radical axes; homopethic centres and systems of circles; parataxy and parallelism; Gauss' proof of defect area theorem; much more, with exceptional clarity. 126 problems at chapter ends. 133 figures. xvi + 274pp. 5⅜ x 8.   S460 Paperbound **$1.50**

THE FOUNDATIONS OF EUCLIDEAN GEOMETRY, H. G. Forder. First connected, rigorous account in light of modern analysis, establishing propositions without recourse to empiricism, without multiplying hypotheses. Based on tools of 19th and 20th century mathematicians, who made it possible to remedy gaps and complexities, recognize problems not earlier discerned. Begins with important relationship of number systems in geometrical figures. Considers classes, relations, linear order, natural numbers, axioms for magnitudes, groups, quasi-fields, fields, non-Archimedian systems, the axiom system (at length), particular axioms (two chapters on the Parallel Axioms), constructions, congruence, similarity, etc. Lists: axioms employed, constructions, symbols in frequent use. 295pp. 5⅜ x 8.
S481 Paperbound **$2.00**

CALCULUS, FUNCTION THEORY (REAL AND COMPLEX), FOURIER THEORY

FIVE VOLUME "THEORY OF FUNCTIONS" SET BY KONRAD KNOPP. Provides complete, readily followed account of theory of functions. Proofs given concisely, yet without sacrifice of completeness or rigor. These volumes used as texts by such universities as M.I.T., Chicago, N.Y. City College, many others. "Excellent introduction . . . remarkably readable, concise, clear, rigorous," J. of the American Statistical Association.

ELEMENTS OF THE THEORY OF FUNCTIONS, Konrad Knopp. Provides background for further volumes in this set, or texts on similar level. Partial contents: Foundations, system of complex numbers and Gaussian plane of numbers, Riemann sphere of numbers, mapping by linear functions, normal forms, the logarithm, cyclometric functions, binomial series. "Not only for the young student, but also for the student who knows all about what is in it," Mathematical Journal. 140pp. 5⅜ x 8.   S154 Paperbound **$1.35**

THEORY OF FUNCTIONS, PART I, Konrad Knopp. With volume II, provides coverage of basic concepts and theorems. Partial contents: numbers and points, functions of a complex variable, integral of a continuous function, Cauchy's intergral theorem, Cauchy's integral formulae, series with variable terms, expansion and analytic function in a power series, analytic continuation and complete definition of analytic functions, Laurent expansion, types of singularities. vii + 146pp. 5⅜ x 8.   S156 Paperbound **$1.35**

THEORY OF FUNCTIONS, PART II, Konrad Knopp. Application and further development of general theory, special topics. Single valued functions, entire, Weierstrass. Meromorphic functions: Mittag-Leffler. Periodic functions. Multiple valued functions. Riemann surfaces. Algebraic functions. Analytical configurations, Riemann surface. x + 150pp. 5⅜ x 8.
S157 Paperbound **$1.35**

PROBLEM BOOK IN THE THEORY OF FUNCTIONS, VOLUME I, Konrad Knopp. Problems in elementary theory, for use with Knopp's "Theory of Functions," or any other text. Arranged according to increasing difficulty. Fundamental concepts, sequences of numbers and infinite series, complex variable, integral theorems, development in series, conformal mapping. Answers. viii + 126pp. 5⅜ x 8.
S 158 **Paperbound $1.35**

PROBLEM BOOK IN THE THEORY OF FUNCTIONS, VOLUME II, Konrad Knopp. Advanced theory of functions, to be used with Knopp's "Theory of Functions," or comparable text. Singularities, entire and meromorphic functions, periodic, analytic, continuation, multiple-valued functions, Riemann surfaces, conformal mapping. Includes section of elementary problems. "The difficult task of selecting . . . problems just within the reach of the beginner is here masterfully accomplished," AM. MATH. SOC. Answers. 138pp. 5⅜ x 8.
S159 Paperbound **$1.35**

ADVANCED CALCULUS, E. B. Wilson. Still recognized as one of most comprehensive, useful texts. Immense amount of well-represented, fundamental material, including chapters on vector functions, ordinary differential equations, special functions, calculus of variations, etc., which are excellent introductions to these areas. Requires only one year of calculus. Over 1300 exercises cover both pure math and applications to engineering and physical problems. Ideal reference, refresher. 54 page introductory review. ix + 566pp. 5⅜ x 8.
S504 Paperbound **$2.45**

LECTURES ON THE THEORY OF ELLIPTIC FUNCTIONS, H. Hancock. Reissue of only book in English with so extensive a coverage, especially of Abel, Jacobi, Legendre, Weierstrass, Hermite, Liouville, and Riemann. Unusual fullness of treatment, plus applications as well as theory in discussing universe of elliptic integrals, originating in works of Abel and Jacobi. Use is made of Riemann to provide most general theory. 40-page table of formulas. 76 figures. xxiii + 498pp. 5⅜ x 8.
S483 Paperbound **$2.55**

THEORY OF FUNCTIONALS AND OF INTEGRAL AND INTEGRO-DIFFERENTIAL EQUATIONS, Vito Volterra. Unabridged republication of only English translation. General theory of functions depending on continuous set of values of another function. Based on author's concept of transition from finite number of variables to a continually infinite number. Includes much material on calculus of variations. Begins with fundamentals, examines generalization of analytic functions, functional derivative equations, applications, other directions of theory, etc. New introduction by G. C. Evans. Biography, criticism of Volterra's work by E. Whittaker. xxxx + 226pp. 5⅜ x 8.
S502 Paperbound **$1.75**

AN INTRODUCTION TO FOURIER METHODS AND THE LAPLACE TRANSFORMATION, Philip Franklin. Concentrates on essentials, gives broad view, suitable for most applications. Requires only knowledge of calculus. Covers complex qualities with methods of computing elementary functions for complex values of argument and finding approximations by charts; Fourier series; harmonic anaylsis; much more. Methods are related to physical problems of heat flow, vibrations, electrical transmission, electromagnetic radiation, etc. 828 problems, answers. Formerly entitled "Fourier Methods." x + 289pp. 5⅜ x 8.
S452 Paperbound **$1.75**

THE ANALYTICAL THEORY OF HEAT, Joseph Fourier. This book, which revolutionized mathematical physics, has been used by generations of mathematicians and physicists interested in heat or application of Fourier integral. Covers cause and reflection of rays of heat, radiant heating, heating of closed spaces, use of trigonometric series in theory of heat, Fourier integral, etc. Translated by Alexander Freeman. 20 figures. xxii + 466pp. 5⅜ x 8.
S93 Paperbound **$2.00**

ELLIPTIC INTEGRALS, H. Hancock. Invaluable in work involving differential equations with cubics, quatrics under root sign, where elementary calculus methods are inadequate. Practical solutions to problems in mathematics, engineering, physics; differential equations requiring integration of Lamé's, Briot's, or Bouquet's equations; determination of arc of ellipse, hyperbola, lemiscate; solutions of problems in elastics; motion of a projectile under resistance varying as the cube of the velocity; pendulums; more. Exposition in accordance with Legendre-Jacobi theory. Rigorous discussion of Legendre transformations. 20 figures. 5 place table. 104pp. 5⅜ x 8.
S484 Paperbound **$1.25**

THE TAYLOR SERIES, AN INTRODUCTION TO THE THEORY OF FUNCTIONS OF A COMPLEX VARIABLE, P. Dienes. Uses Taylor series to approach theory of functions, using ordinary calculus only, except in last 2 chapters. Starts with introduction to real variable and complex algebra, derives properties of infinite series, complex differentiation, integration, etc. Covers biuniform mapping, overconvergence and gap theorems, Taylor series on its circle of convergence, etc. Unabridged corrected reissue of first edition. 186 examples, many fully worked out. 67 figures. xii + 555pp. 5⅜ x 8.
S391 Paperbound **$2.75**

LINEAR INTEGRAL EQUATIONS, W. V. Lovitt. Systematic survey of general theory, with some application to differential equations, calculus of variations, problems of math, physics. Includes: integral equation of 2nd kind by successive substitutions; Fredholm's equation as ratio of 2 integral series in lambda, applications of the Fredholm theory, Hilbert-Schmidt theory of symmetric kernels, application, etc. Neumann, Dirichlet, vibratory problems. ix + 253pp. 5⅜ x 8.
S175 Clothbound **$3.50**
S176 Paperbound **$1.60**

DOVER SCIENCE BOOKS

DICTIONARY OF CONFORMAL REPRESENTATIONS, H. Kober. Developed by British Admiralty to solve Laplace's equation in 2 dimensions. Scores of geometrical forms and transformations for electrical engineers, Joukowski aerofoil for aerodynamics, Schwartz-Christoffel transformations for hydro-dynamics, transcendental functions. Contents classified according to analytical functions describing transformations with corresponding regions. Glossary. Topological index. 447 diagrams. 6⅛ x 9¼.   .S160 Paperbound **$2.00**

ELEMENTS OF THE THEORY OF REAL FUNCTIONS, J. E. Littlewood. Based on lectures at Trinity College, Cambridge, this book has proved extremely successful in introducing graduate students to modern theory of functions. Offers full and concise coverage of classes and cardinal numbers, well ordered series, other types of series, and elements of the theory of sets of points. 3rd revised edition. vii + 71pp. 5⅜ x 8.   S171 Clothbound **$2.85**
                                                                        S172 Paperbound **$1.25**

INFINITE SEQUENCES AND SERIES, Konrad Knopp. 1st publication in any language. Excellent introduction to 2 topics of modern mathematics, designed to give student background to penetrate further alone. Sequences and sets, real and complex numbers, etc. Functions of a real and complex variable. Sequences and series. Infinite series. Convergent power series. Expansion of elementary functions. Numerical evaluation of series. v + 186pp. 5⅜ x 8.
                                                                        S152 Clothbound **$3.50**
                                                                        S153 Paperbound **$1.75**

THE THEORY AND FUNCTIONS OF A REAL VARIABLE AND THE THEORY OF FOURIER'S SERIES, E. W .Hobson. One of the best introductions to set theory and various aspects of functions and Fourier's series. Requires only a good background in calculus. Exhaustive coverage of: metric and descriptive properties of sets of points; transfinite numbers and order types; functions of a real variable; the Riemann and Lebesgue integrals; sequences and series of numbers; power-series; functions representable by series sequences of continuous functions; trigonometrical series; representation of functions by Fourier's series; and much more. "The best possible guide," Nature. Vol. I: 88 detailed examples, 10 figures. Index. xv + 736pp. Vol. II: 117 detailed examples, 13 figures. x + 780pp. 6⅛ x 9¼.
                                                                        Vol. I: S387 Paperbound **$3.00**
                                                                        Vol. II: S388 Paperbound **$3.00**

ALMOST PERIODIC FUNCTIONS, A. S. Besicovitch. Unique and important summary by a well known mathematician covers in detail the two stages of development in Bohr's theory of almost periodic functions: (1) as a generalization of pure periodicity, with results and proofs; (2) the work done by Stepanof, Wiener, Weyl, and Bohr in generalizing the theory. xi + 180pp. 5⅜ x 8.   S18 Paperbound **$1.75**

INTRODUCTION TO THE THEORY OF FOURIER'S SERIES AND INTEGRALS, H. S. Carslaw. 3rd revised edition, an outgrowth of author's courses at Cambridge. Historical introduction, rational, irrational numbers, infinite sequences and series, functions of a single variable, definite integral, Fourier series, and similar topics. Appendices discuss practical harmonic analysis, periodogram analysis, Lebesgue's theory. 84 examples. xiii + 368pp. 5⅜ x 8.
                                                                        S48 Paperbound **$2.00**

SYMBOLIC LOGIC

THE ELEMENTS OF MATHEMATICAL LOGIC, Paul Rosenbloom. First publication in any language. For mathematically mature readers with no training in symbolic. logic. Development of lectures given at Lund Univ., Sweden, 1948. Partial contents: Logic of classes, fundamental theorems, Boolean algebra, logic of propositions, of propositional functions, expressive languages, combinatory logics, development of math within an object language, paradoxes, theorems of Post, Goedel, Church, and similar topics. iv + 214pp. 5⅜ x 8.
                                                                        S227 Paperbound **$1.45**

INTRODUCTION TO SYMBOLIC LOGIC AND ITS APPLICATION, R. Carnap. Clear, comprehensive, rigorous, by perhaps greatest living master. Symbolic languages analyzed, one constructed. Applications to math (axiom systems for set theory, real, natural numbers), topology (Dedekind, Cantor continuity explanations), physics (general analysis of determination, causality, space-time topology), biology (axiom system for basic concepts). Over 300 exercises. 5 figures. xvi + 241pp. 5⅜ x 8.   S453 Paperbound **$1.85**

AN INTRODUCTION TO SYMBOLIC LOGIC, Susanne K. Langer. Probably clearest book for the philosopher, scientist, layman—no special knowledge of math required. Starts with simplest symbols, goes on to give remarkable grasp of Boole-Schroeder, Russell-Whitehead systems, clearly, quickly. Partial Contents: Forms, Generalization, Classes, Deductive System of Classes, Algebra of Logic, Assumptions of Principia Mathematica, Logistics, Proofs of Theorems, etc. "Clearest . . . simplest introduction . . . the intelligent non-mathematician should have no difficulty," MATHEMATICS GAZETTE. Revised, expanded 2nd edition. Truth-value tables. 368pp. 5⅜ 8.   S164 Paperbound **$1.75**

13

TRIGONOMETRICAL SERIES, Antoni Zygmund. On modern advanced level. Contains carefully organized analyses of trigonometric, orthogonal, Fourier systems of functions, with clear adequate descriptions of summability of Fourier series, proximation theory, conjugate series, convergence, divergence of Fourier series. Especially valuable for Russian, Eastern European coverage. 329pp. 5⅜ x 8.   S290 Paperbound **$1.50**

THE LAWS OF THOUGHT, George Boole. This book founded symbolic logic some 100 years ago. It is the 1st significant attempt to apply logic to all aspects of human endeavour. Partial contents: derivation of laws, signs and laws, interpretations, eliminations, conditions of a perfect method, analysis, Aristotelian logic, probability, and similar topics. xvii + 424pp. 5⅜ x 8.   S28 Paperbound **$2.00**

SYMBOLIC LOGIC, C. I. Lewis, C. H. Langford. 2nd revised edition of probably most cited book in symbolic logic. Wide coverage of entire field; one of fullest treatments of paradoxes; plus much material not available elsewhere. Basic to volume is distinction between logic of extensions and intensions. Considerable emphasis on converse substitution, while matrix system presents supposition of variety of non-Aristotelian logics. Especially valuable sections on strict limitations, existence theorems. Partial contents: Boole-Schroeder algebra; truth value systems, the matrix method; implication and deductibility; general theory of propositions; etc. "Most valuable," Times, London. 506pp. 5⅜ x 8.   S170 Paperbound **$2.00**

GROUP THEORY AND LINEAR ALGEBRA, SETS, ETC.

LECTURES ON THE ICOSAHEDRON AND THE SOLUTION OF EQUATIONS OF THE FIFTH DEGREE, Felix Klein. Solution of quintics in terms of rotations of regular icosahedron around its axes of symmetry. A classic, indispensable source for those interested in higher algebra, geometry, crystallography. Considerable explanatory material included. 230 footnotes, mostly bibliography. "Classical monograph . . . detailed, readable book," Math. Gazette. 2nd edition. xvi + 289pp. 5⅜ x 8.   S314 Paperbound **$1.85**

INTRODUCTION TO THE THEORY OF GROUPS OF FINITE ORDER, R. Carmichael. Examines fundamental theorems and their applications. Beginning with sets, systems, permutations, etc., progresses in easy stages through important types of groups: Abelian, prime power, permutation, etc. Except 1 chapter where matrices are desirable, no higher math is needed. 783 exercises, problems. xvi + 447pp. 5⅜ x 8.   S299 Clothbound **$3.95**
                                                                     S300 Paperbound **$2.00**

THEORY OF GROUPS OF FINITE ORDER, W. Burnside. First published some 40 years ago, still one of clearest introductions. Partial contents: permutations, groups independent of representation, composition series of a group, isomorphism of a group with itself, Abelian groups, prime power groups, permutation groups, invariants of groups of linear substitution, graphical representation, etc. "Clear and detailed discussion . . . numerous problems which are instructive," Design News. xxiv + 512pp. 5⅜ x 8.   S38 Paperbound **$2.45**

COMPUTATIONAL METHODS OF LINEAR ALGEBRA, V. N. Faddeeva, translated by C. D. Benster. 1st English translation of unique, valuable work, only one in English presenting systematic exposition of most important methods of linear algebra—classical, contemporary. Details of deriving numerical solutions of problems in mathematical physics. Theory and practice. Includes survey of necessary background, most important methods of solution, for exact, iterative groups. One of most valuable features is 23 tables, triple checked for accuracy, unavailable elsewhere. Translator's note. x + 252pp. 5⅜ x 8.   S424 Paperbound **$1.95**

THE CONTINUUM AND OTHER TYPES OF SERIAL ORDER, E. V. Huntington. This famous book gives a systematic elementary account of the modern theory of the continuum as a type of serial order. Based on the Cantor-Dedekind ordinal theory, which requires no technical knowledge of higher mathematics, it offers an easily followed analysis of ordered classes, discrete and dense series, continuous series, Cantor's transfinite numbers. "Admirable introduction to the rigorous theory of the continuum . . . reading easy," Science Progress. 2nd edition. viii + 82pp. 5⅜ x 8.   S129 Clothbound **$2.75**
                                                                     S130 Paperbound **$1.00**

THEORY OF SETS, E. Kamke. Clearest, amplest introduction in English, well suited for independent study. Subdivisions of main theory, such as theory of sets of points, are discussed, but emphasis is on general theory. Partial contents: rudiments of set theory, arbitrary sets, their cardinal numbers, ordered sets, their order types, well-ordered sets, their cardinal numbers. vii + 144pp. 5⅜ x 8.   S141 Paperbound **$1.35**

CONTRIBUTIONS TO THE FOUNDING OF THE THEORY OF TRANSFINITE NUMBERS, Georg Cantor. These papers founded a new branch of mathematics. The famous articles of 1895-7 are translated, with an 82-page introduction by P. E. B. Jourdain dealing with Cantor, the background of his discoveries, their results, future possibiilties. ix + 211pp. 5⅜ x 8.
                                                                     S45 Paperbound **$1.25**

DOVER SCIENCE BOOKS

NUMERICAL AND GRAPHICAL METHODS, TABLES

JACOBIAN ELLIPTIC FUNCTION TABLES, L. M. Milne-Thomson. Easy-to-follow, practical, not only useful numerical tables, but complete elementary sketch of application of elliptic functions. Covers description of principle properties; complete elliptic integrals; Fourier series, expansions; periods, zeros, poles, residues, formulas for special values of argument; cubic, quartic polynomials; pendulum problem; etc. Tables, graphs form body of book: Graph, 5 figure table of elliptic function sn (u m); cn (u m); dn (u m). 8 figure table of complete elliptic integrals K, K', E, E', nome q. 7 figure table of Jacobian zeta-function Z(u). 3 figures. xi + 123pp. 5⅜ x 8.   S194 Paperbound **$1.35**

TABLES OF FUNCTIONS WITH FORMULAE AND CURVES, E. Jahnke, F. Emde. Most comprehensive 1-volume English text collection of tables, formulae, curves of transcendent functions. 4th corrected edition, new 76-page section giving tables, formulae for elementary functions not in other English editions. Partial contents: sine, cosine, logarithmic integral; error integral; elliptic integrals; theta functions; Legendre, Bessel, Riemann, Mathieu, hypergeometric functions; etc. "Out-of-the-way functions for which we know no other source." Scientific Computing Service, Ltd. 212 figures. 400pp. 5⅝ x 8⅜.   S133 Paperbound **$2.00**

MATHEMATICAL TABLES, H. B. Dwight. Covers in one volume almost every function of importance in applied mathematics, engineering, physical sciences. Three extremely fine tables of the three trig functions, inverses, to 1000th of radian; natural, common logs; squares, cubes; hyperbolic functions, inverses; (a^2 + b^2) exp. ½a; complete elliptical integrals of 1st, 2nd kind; sine, cosine integrals; exponential integrals; $Ei(x)$ and $Ei(-x)$; binomial coefficients; factorials to 250; surface zonal harmonics, first derivatives; Bernoulli, Euler numbers, their logs to base of 10; Gamma function; normal probability integral; over 60pp. Bessel functions; Riemann zeta function. Each table with formulae generally used, sources of more extensive tables, interpolation data, etc. Over half have columns of differences, to facilitate interpolation. viii + 231pp. 5⅜ x 8.   S445 Paperbound **$1.75**

PRACTICAL ANALYSIS, GRAPHICAL AND NUMERICAL METHODS, F. A. Willers. Immensely practical hand-book for engineers. How to interpolate, use various methods of numerical differentiation and integration, determine roots of a single algebraic equation, system of linear equations, use empirical formulas, integrate differential equations, etc. Hundreds of short-cuts for arriving at numerical solutions. Special section on American calculating machines, by T. W. Simpson. Translation by R. T. Beyer. 132 illustrations. 422pp. 5⅜ x 8.
S273 Paperbound **$2.00**

NUMERICAL SOLUTIONS OF DIFFERENTIAL EQUATIONS, H. Levy, E. A. Baggott. Comprehensive collection of methods for solving ordinary differential equations of first and higher order. 2 requirements: practical, easy to grasp; more rapid than school methods. Partial contents: graphical integration of differential equations, graphical methods for detailed solution. Numerical solution. Simultaneous equations and equations of 2nd and higher orders. "Should be in the hands of all in research and applied mathematics, teaching," Nature. 21 figures. viii + 238pp. 5⅜ x 8.   S168 Paperbound **$1.75**

NUMERICAL INTEGRATION OF DIFFERENTIAL EQUATIONS, Bennet, Milne, Bateman. Unabridged republication of original prepared for National Research Council. New methods of integration by 3 leading mathematicians: "The Interpolational Polynomial," "Successive Approximation," A. A. Bennett, "Step-by-step Methods of Integration," W. W. Milne. "Methods for Partial Differential Equations," H. Bateman. Methods for partial differential equations, solution of differential equations to non-integral values of a parameter will interest mathematicians, physicists. 288 footnotes, mostly bibliographical. 235 item classified bibliography. 108pp. 5⅜ x 8.   S305 Paperbound **$1.35**